Amazing Logic Puzzles

Norman D. Willis

Illustrated by Jim Sharpe

STERLING PUBLISHING CO., INC.
NEW YORK

To my wife, Judith,
whose support and critique have been invaluable.

Library of Congress Cataloging-in-Publication Data

Willis, Norman D.
   Amazing logic puzzles / Norman D. Willis ; illustrated by Jim
Sharpe.
     p.   cm.
   ISBN 0-8069-0564-6
   1. Puzzles. 2. Logic. I. Sharpe, Jim. II. Title.
GV1493.W4965   1994
793.73—dc20   93-39592
                                           CIP

Cover by Bob Eggleton

10 9 8 7 6 5 4 3 2 1

Published by Sterling Publishing Company, Inc.
387 Park Avenue South, New York, N.Y. 10016
Text © 1994 by Norman D. Willis
Illustrations © 1994 by Jim Sharpe
Distributed in Canada by Sterling Publishing
% Canadian Manda Group, P.O. Box 920, Station U
Toronto, Ontario, Canada M8Z 5P9
Distributed in Great Britain and Europe by Cassell PLC
Villiers House, 41/47 Strand, London WC2N 5JE, England
Distributed in Australia by Capricorn Link (Australia) Pty Ltd.
P.O. Box 6651, Baulkham Hills, Business Centre, NSW 2153, Australia
Manufactured in the United States of America
All rights reserved

Sterling ISBN 0-8069-0564-6

Contents

Before You Begin

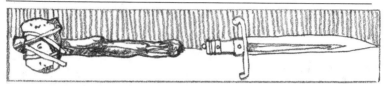

Logic puzzles are fun and stimulating because they are challenging. At the same time, and perhaps more importantly, they can be helpful in expanding the mental capabilities of people of all ages. Solving and enjoying the puzzles in this book will help strengthen the solver's mental power and ability to think logically. The puzzles have been developed with this thought in mind.

Solving these logic puzzles requires no specialized knowledge or mathematical skill beyond a basic understanding of addition, subtraction and multiplication. Solutions do not depend on memory, word play or deception. They rely only on thought and mental ingenuity. What is required of you is that you conscientiously apply your own natural skill at deductive reasoning.

As you work your way through this book you will encounter six kinds of logic puzzles, grouped by category, as follows:

Hypotheses

Suppositions that may or may not be valid are the key ingredients in these puzzles. Your challenge in each puzzle is to determine which hypotheses are invalid.

Who did it?

Each of these puzzles contains statements by suspects of a crime. Your task is to determine who is guilty.

Letters for digits

These are basic addition, subtraction and multiplication problems in which the numbers have been replaced by letters. The challenge is to identify the digits.

Standards of veracity

Individuals who have different standards of veracity afford a vehicle for challenging logic puzzles. Your task is to determine who has what standard of truthfulness or falsity.

Arrangement in order

This type of logic puzzle involves a series of statements that describe, item by item, the order in which things or persons belong. Arranging the elements successfully may not be as easy as it sounds.

Fragments of information

These puzzles contain statements that provide limited amounts of relevant information. In total, they contain just enough data for you to formulate the solution.

Within each category the puzzles are arranged in order of difficulty starting with the more easily solved and progressing to the most challenging. They are rated according to variety and multiplicity of data to be considered, and amount of innovativeness needed. They are graded from one to three asterisks as follows:

> *   Challenging
> * *   Tantalizing
> * * * Mind-Expanding!

A "Hints" section comes after the puzzles. It contains suggestions for approaching the puzzles of each type as well as some specific guides relating to specific puzzles. If you think you need help in solving a particular puzzle, a review of the considerations leading to the solution may help you to solve it and similar puzzles. It may also help you in developing your puzzle-solving ability.

The final section contains solutions. Where appropriate, methods and rationales supporting the solutions are afforded.

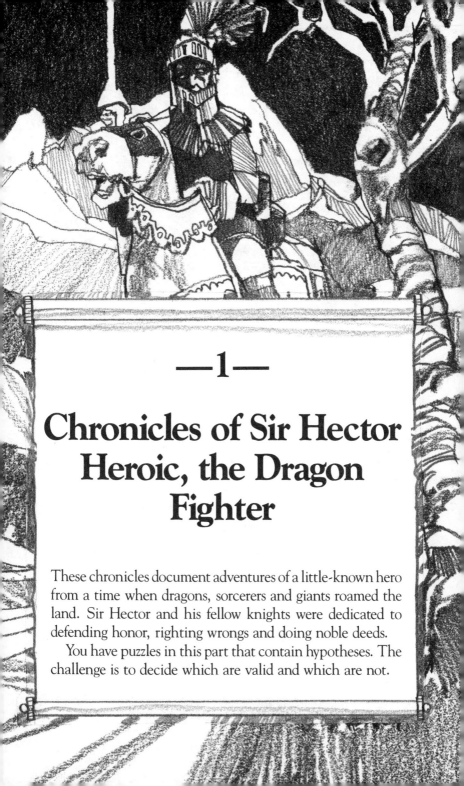

—1—

Chronicles of Sir Hector Heroic, the Dragon Fighter

These chronicles document adventures of a little-known hero from a time when dragons, sorcerers and giants roamed the land. Sir Hector and his fellow knights were dedicated to defending honor, righting wrongs and doing noble deeds.

You have puzzles in this part that contain hypotheses. The challenge is to decide which are valid and which are not.

P1–1 Giants or Dragons?*

During Sir Hector's time, knights were frequently called upon to prove their courage, strength and prowess. To this end, fighting giants and dragons were important activities.

Sir Hector and his fellow knights had a continual debate as to which adversaries, giants or dragons, were the more dangerous and, therefore, presented the more noble challenge. Two of the knights preferred fighting giants and two preferred fighting dragons. It would be too much to attempt to settle this dispute, but from the statements below, can you determine which two knights preferred fighting giants and which two preferred fighting dragons?

1. If Sir Hector preferred giants, then Sir Bold and Sir Gallant preferred dragons.
2. If Sir Bold preferred giants, then Sir Hector and Sir Gallant preferred dragons.
3. If Sir Gallant preferred giants, then Sir Hector and Sir Able preferred dragons.
4. If Sir Able preferred giants, then Sir Gallant and Sir Hector preferred dragons.

(Hint on page 72)
(Solution on page 86)

P1–2   Encounter with the Black Knight*

The truculent Black Knight was a veritable giant of a man. As tall and wide as a doorway and weighing over 20 stone, he struck fear throughout the land.

The courageous Sir Hector confronted the Black Knight on a narrow bridge over a river as both were attempting to cross in different directions. Neither would give way, and the two engaged in battle.

Based on the statements below, determine the outcome of the battle.

1. If the Black Knight was defeated by Sir Hector, then he vowed revenge.

2. If the two knights fought to a draw, then they put away their weapons and agreed not to fight again.

3. If Sir Hector slipped and fell into the river, then he escaped.

4. The Black Knight vowed revenge, unless the two knights did not fight to a draw.

(Hint on page 72)
(Solution on pages 86–87)

P1–3   The Fable of Sir Hector and the Giant*

Many tales of the feats of Sir Hector have been passed by word of mouth from generation to generation. This is one of those tales:

> Lodegan the giant, who was regarded with terror throughout the land, took cattle and sheep from wherever he found them. The farmers and shepherds of the province appealed, but with small prospect of success, for a champion who, with his strength and prowess, would rid them of the fierce giant. Sir Hector accepted the mission gladly, as he was wont to do. He made ready his arms and rode forth without delay.
>
> The goodly knight engaged Lodegan in battle and, with his swiftness, was able to smite the giant repeatedly with his lance and safely withdraw. Lodegan, who was by nature slow to anger, at last lost patience with his irritating opponent. He inhaled mightily and blew Sir Hector and his horse a distance of several leagues away.
>
> Sir Hector recovered himself, remounted his steed and headed back to resume the fray, as he was a true knight and would not shame himself yielding to a foe. When he arrived back at the location of the battle, the giant was nowhere to be seen, nor was he found in those parts again.

From the statements that follow, determine what became of the giant.

1. If Lodegan, who was very old even for a giant, totally collapsed as a result of his exertion and disappeared into

the surrounding terrain, then the battle with Sir Hector lasted from daylight till dark.

2. If the giant was in reality Mordin the sorcerer in disguise and he returned to his natural form, then the battle took place at sunup.

3. If the giant, who had magical powers, turned into a bird and flew away, then the battle took place at sundown.

4. If the battle took place at midday, then the giant left and retired to the mountains to spend his days eating nuts and berries.

5. If the battle took place at sundown or lasted from daylight till dark, then the giant was in reality Mordin the sorcerer in disguise and he returned to his natural form.

6. The giant, who had magical powers, turned into a bird and flew away, if the battle took place at sunup.

(Hints on page 73)
(Solution on page 87)

P1–4   A Victorious Encounter with a Dragon*

A dragon was frightening livestock and destroying crops by blowing smoke and flames across the land. Sir Hector, Sir Able and Sir Bold undertook to confront the ferocious beast. However, they decided that only one of the three should fight the dragon, that being the noble and knightly thing to do. The second knight would assist with such things as replacing broken lances and providing bandages, and the third knight would observe and record the deed.

The ancient dragon was not much interested in the confrontation. After a brief skirmish, he complained of too much smoke blowing back into his eyes, and he quit the battle and flew away.

There was much rejoicing in the villages and the three knights received adulation befitting heroes. There was some confusion, however, as to which knight had fought the dragon, which one had assisted and which one had observed.

Based on the following statements, can you resolve the confusion?

1. If Sir Hector observed the battle, then Sir Able fought the dragon.
2. If Sir Able observed the battle, then Sir Bold fought the dragon.
3. If Sir Hector fought the dragon, then Sir Bold assisted.
4. If Sir Bold fought the dragon, then Sir Able assisted.
5. If Sir Hector assisted, then Sir Able observed the battle.

(Hints on page 73)
(Solution on pages 87–88)

P1–5   Sir Hector's Steed*

Sir Hector's horse was his most prized possession. The noble animal, with its courage and speed, served on several occasions to turn a sure defeat into a victory. Based on the statements below, can you determine the name and color of Sir Hector's steed?

1. If the color was either black or grey, then the name was Charger.
2. If the color was either black-and-white or palomino, then the name was Endeavor.
3. If the name was Valiant, then the color was either black-and-white or black.
4. If the name was Charger, then the color was grey or palomino.
5. The color was bay or grey, if the name was Endeavor.
6. The color was not white, if the name was not Valiant.
7. If the color was bay or grey, then the name was Charger.

(Hints on page 73)
(Solution on pages 88–89)

P1–6 Knights' Shields**

The shields of Sir Hector, Sir Able, Sir Bold and Sir Gallant were of different colors. From the statements below, determine the colors of each knight's shield.

1. If Sir Gallant's shield was blue and white, then Sir Able's shield was black and silver.
2. If Sir Bold's shield was green and gold, then Sir Hector's shield was blue and white.
3. If Sir Bold's shield was blue and white, then Sir Hector's shield was black and silver.
4. If Sir Hector's shield was red and white, then Sir Gallant's shield was not green and gold.
5. If Sir Hector's shield was not green and gold, then Sir Able's shield was blue and white.
6. If Sir Able's shield was black and silver, then Sir Bold's shield was blue and white.
7. If Sir Gallant's shield was black and silver, then Sir Bold's shield was green and gold.

(Hints on pages 73–74)
(Solution on pages 89–90)

P1-7 The Jousting Competition**

At a time when there were no noble deeds to accomplish, Sir Hector and his fellow knights, Sir Able, Sir Bold and Sir Gallant, decided that, to stay in condition, they would have a jousting competition among themselves. The winner was to be the knight who was the last to remain on his horse.

Based on the following statements, which knight won the competition, which one was the third to be unhorsed, which one was the second to be unhorsed, and which one was the first to be unhorsed?

1. If Sir Gallant was either the second or the first knight to be unhorsed, then Sir Able was the third knight to be unhorsed.
2. If either Sir Gallant or Sir Hector was the first knight to be unhorsed, then Sir Bold was the third knight to be unhorsed.
3. If Sir Bold was the first knight to be unhorsed, then Sir Hector was the third knight to be unhorsed.
4. If Sir Able was the winner, then Sir Hector was neither the second nor the first knight to be unhorsed.
5. If Sir Able was the third knight to be unhorsed, then Sir Bold was either the winner or the second knight to be unhorsed.
6. If Sir Bold was either the winner or the third knight to be unhorsed, then Sir Hector was the second knight to be unhorsed and Sir Gallant was the first knight to be unhorsed.
7. If Sir Able was the first knight to be unhorsed, then Sir Gallant was neither the winner nor the third knight to be unhorsed.

(Hints on page 74)
(Solution on pages 90–91)

P1-8   Who Was Whose Squire?**

Sir Hector and his three fellow knights each had a squire who provided valuable assistance in many ways. The problem was that, since the four squires dressed alike and looked very much alike, it was sometimes difficult to tell who was whose squire.

Given the following statements, can you determine which squire assisted which knight?

1. If Alf was not Sir Hector's squire, Del was Sir Hector's squire.
2. Del was not Sir Hector's squire, if Alf was Sir Able's squire.
3. If Cal was not Sir Gallant's squire, Del was Sir Bold's squire.
4. If Del was Sir Able's squire, Bo was Sir Hector's squire.
5. Cal was not Sir Able's squire, if Bo was not Sir Hector's squire.
6. Cal was Sir Hector's squire, if Del was Sir Bold's squire.

(Hints on page 74)
(Solution on page 92)

P1–9   Which Knights Were Honored?**

The major event of the year was the invitational tournament among knights, which attracted participants from throughout the land. The tournament was organized in several series of jousts, each series requiring use of a different weapon. Following the tournament, the knights who were ranked among the top five in the competition were honored. The top five knights entered every series of jousts, and were not unhorsed or felled at any time.

Of six knights, Sir Able, Sir Bold, Sir Gallant, Sir Hector, Sir Resolute and Sir Victor, three were among the top five. These included the winner, the knight who was ranked third and the knight who was ranked fifth. Based on the statements below, which three knights were honored and where did each rank in the tournament competition?

1. If Sir Gallant was the winner, Sir Bold ranked third.
2. Sir Hector won the tournament, unless Sir Able neglected to bring his battle-axe and had to sit out that series of jousts.
3. If Sir Victor was not ranked fifth, then neither Sir Bold nor Sir Gallant was among the five knights who were ranked.
4. If Sir Resolute was not among those ranked, then Sir Bold was the winner.
5. Sir Able won the tournament, unless Sir Hector had to remount his horse during any of his jousts.
6. If Sir Resolute was ranked third, then Sir Victor was the winner.
7. If Sir Resolute was the winner, then Sir Bold was ranked fifth.

(Hints on pages 74–75)
(Solution on pages 92–93)

P1–10   Confrontation with Mordin the Sorcerer***

Sir Hector and his three comrades, Sir Able, Sir Bold and Sir Gallant, resolved to defeat the evil sorcerer Mordin, and drive him from the land. Because of the extreme difficulty of this task, they recruited a fifth knight, Sir Victor, to assist them.

The five knights confronted the powerful Mordin, but were soundly beaten. The first two knights to be overcome were simultaneously turned into pigs by the sorcerer, and the next two knights who were overcome were simultaneously turned into goats. At this point, Mordin's magical powers were severely depleted, and he was only able to turn the fifth knight into a half knight/half goat.

Mordin realized that, had there been a sixth knight in the fray, the tide of battle might have turned against him. This concern, and the knights' courage and determination, caused Mordin so much anxiety that he left the land, not to return. As for the knights, the spells were only temporary and, after a few hours, they turned back into their natural forms.

From the statements below, determine which knights were turned into which animals.

1. Sir Able and Sir Gallant, who was not turned into a pig, met the same fate, if Sir Bold and Sir Hector met the same fate.
2. If Sir Victor was not turned into a goat, then Sir Able was turned into a pig.
3. Sir Victor was turned into a goat, if Sir Hector and Sir Gallant met the same fate.
4. Sir Hector was not overcome at the same time as Sir Able, who was not overcome at a later time than Sir Bold.
5. If Sir Hector and Sir Victor met the same fate, then so did Sir Gallant and Sir Bold.
6. If Sir Victor and Sir Gallant met the same fate, then Sir Hector was turned into a pig.

(Hints on page 75)
(Solution on pages 94–95)

P1–11 Final Encounter with the Black Knight***

The villainous Black Knight had pilfered and plundered across the land. It was up to Sir Hector to do something about it.

Sir Hector confronted the Black Knight, and a raging battle ensued. During their encounter, the two knights fought in three separate locations: the village of Farmwell, the open plain, and deep in the forest, not necessarily in that order. At each location Sir Hector, who was no match for the large and mighty Black

Knight, was overcome. However, each time, after a brief rest, he pursued his adversary and confronted him again. Finally, the Black Knight became so frustrated by Sir Hector's refusal to yield (and perhaps impressed by his courage and determination) that he left for distant places and was not seen again. The two knights used swords, lances and staves, but only one weapon at each location.

Based on the following statements, what was the sequence of the locations at which the three confrontations took place, and what type of weapon was used each time?

1. The second confrontation between the two knights was on the open plain, unless the third confrontation was not in the village of Farmwell.
2. If swords were used in the confrontation deep in the forest, then lances were not used in the confrontation in the village of Farmwell.
3. If staves were not used in the first confrontation, then lances were not used in the second confrontation.
4. If staves were not used in the confrontation in the village of Farmwell, then swords were used in the confrontation deep in the forest.
5. Lances were not used in the second confrontation, unless swords were not used in the third confrontation.
6. If the first confrontation was not deep in the forest, then the second confrontation was on the open plain.

(Hints on pages 75–76)
(Solution on pages 95–96)

—2—
The Planet Dranac

The Planet Dranac lies far beyond the known solar system. It has its own unique beings and civilization.

It is apparent that Dranac is far behind Earth in technological development. As well, Dranacians have less respect for honesty. Deception and crimes are commonplace among the inhabitants.

These puzzles will deal with statements by suspects of crimes. Finding the solutions will depend on determining who is telling the truth and who is lying.

P2–1   Duplgoose Eggs*

Duplgooses, small farm animals, lay eggs only occasionally, although in pairs. Their eggs, an important food source on Dranac, are a highly valued commodity.

A basket of duplgoose eggs has been stolen from the open market in the local village. There are four suspects, and each makes one statement, although only one of the four speaks truthfully. The guilty one can be deduced from their statements below.

A: B did it.
B: D did it.
C: I did it.
D: Either A or C is the guilty one.

Did C do it? If not, who did?

(Hints on page 76)
(Solution on pages 96–97)

P2–2   Huffalon Thefts*

Huffalons, great sturdy beasts that are used for riding, pulling carts and carrying bundles, are the chief source of transportation on the planet.

There have been a number of huffalon thefts in the local village. It is apparent that there are two thieves working together. Several suspects have been identified and two of them are the guilty ones. Each makes one statement below, and four of the six statements are truthful. Only the two guilty parties make false statements.

A: C is guilty.
B: F is not guilty.
C: D is not guilty.
D: B is guilty.
E: A is not guilty.
F: E is not guilty.

Which two are guilty?

(Hints on page 76)
(Solution on page 97)

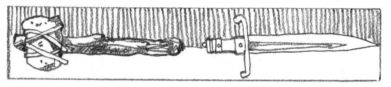

P2–3   Theft in the Overseer's Home*

A crime has occurred in the home of a wealthy village overseer. A valuable collection of ancient Dranacian artifacts has been stolen, and there is no question but that it is an inside job. The suspects are the cook, the housekeeper, the stable hand and the huffalon groom, each of whom makes two statements. The statements made by the stable hand and the housekeeper are false; the huffalon groom makes one truthful statement and one false statement, though in what order is unknown; only the cook makes two truthful statements.

But which suspect is which? They are identified only as A, B, C and D. Their statements follow:

A: 1. I am not the housekeeper.
   2. The huffalon groom is guilty.
B: 1. I am not the huffalon groom.
   2. The housekeeper is guilty.
C: 1. I am not the cook.
   2. The stable hand is guilty.
D: 1. I am not the stable hand.
   2. The cook is guilty.

Which one makes which statements, and who is the guilty party?

(Hints on page 76)
(Solution on pages 97–98)

P2–4   Purloined Prickly Plum Pie*

The inhabitants of Dranac are especially fond of their delicious prickly plum pie. A pie just out of the oven and piping hot was placed on an open window sill to cool. It was not long before it disappeared and was illegally consumed.

There are three suspects who are known to be lovers of prickly plum pie. Each makes three statements as follows, although only one of the guilty party's statements is true. As to the truthfulness of the statements made by the other two suspects, little is known.

A: 1. I was not even there.
   2. C stole the pie.
   3. B helped him eat it.

B: 1. A stole the pie.
   2. The aroma of prickly plum pie is hard to resist.
   3. I did not steal the pie.
C: 1. I do not like prickly plum pie.
   2. B stole the pie.
   3. I did not steal the pie.

Who is guilty?

(Hints on page 76)
(Solution on page 98)

P2–5   Theft on the Farm*

Farm tools and equipment are missing. They have been stolen, and the crime was committed by one of the four farmhands. Their statements are below. Unfortunately, none of them can be depended upon to speak truthfully; each makes one true statement and one false statement, although in which order is unknown.

Farmhand No. 1: 1. I do not trust Farmhand No. 2.
                2. I am certainly not guilty.
Farmhand No. 2: 1. Farmhand No. 1 is guilty.
                2. Farmhand No. 4 did not do it.
Farmhand No. 3: 1. I did not know that the theft had occurred until I heard about it the day it was discovered.
                2. Farmhand No. 1 did not do it.
Farmhand No. 4: 1. Farmhand No. 1 is innocent.
                2. Farmhand No. 3 did not do it.

Who is the guilty one?

(Hints on page 77)
(Solution on page 99)

P2–6   Who Stuffed the Ballot Box?*

In the election for mayor of the village the winning candidate's margin of victory was only three votes. The problem is that there were twenty more votes than there are registered voters. Someone stuffed the ballot box.

Three suspects have been identified, and one of them is guilty. The three are A, the winning candidate's husband; B, the losing candidate's wife; and C, a local character. They make statements, as follows:

A: 1. B had a motive to commit the crime.
      2. C's first statement is true.
      3. B is guilty.

B: 1. My husband was the one hurt by the results; I had no incentive to commit the crime.
      2. C did it.
      3. My husband and I planned to spend several lunar periods on a region-wide tour. We would have had to cancel the trip if he had won the election; I had a motive.

C: 1. I was not near the voting booth on election day.
      2. I am innocent.
      3. B did it.

Considering that each suspect makes only one true statement, can you identify the guilty one?

(Hints on page 77)
(Solution on page 99)

P2–7 Theft in the Village Marketplace*

The economy of Dranac is based on buying, selling and bartering staples in village marketplaces. Produce includes such things as huffalon milk, duplgoose eggs and prickly plums. An armload of prickly plums is taken by a thief while the owner is engaged in negotiating a sale. Three suspects have been identified, one of whom is guilty. They make assertions below, although each suspect makes at least two false statements.

- A: 1. B is guilty.
  - 2. I have met C on several occasions.
  - 3. I have plenty of my own prickly plums.
- B: 1. A and C have never met.
  - 2. I am guilty.
  - 3. A's third statement is false.
- C: 1. I have never met A.
  - 2. A is guilty.
  - 3. B's third statement is true.

Which one is guilty?

(Hints on page 77)
(Solution on page 100)

P2–8   Theft of the Produce Cart**

A cart pulled by a huffalon and loaded with duplgoose eggs for the village market was taken by a thief while the proprietor was busy setting up his sales booth. The stolen property was subsequently recovered, and there are three suspects. They each make assertions below, but no one of them makes all true statements.

A: 1. B is innocent.
2. Everything C will say is false.
3. I am not guilty.
B: 1. I did not do it.
2. C was in the village when it happened.
3. A's second statement is false.
C: 1. A is the thief.
2. I was not even near the village when it happened.
3. I am innocent.

One of the three is guilty, but which one?

(Hints on page 77)
(Solution on page 100)

P2–9   Attempted Sabotage**

A group of space travellers landed on the planet, but were not welcomed by all inhabitants. Someone tried to damage one of the airlocks on the travellers' spaceship. There are three suspects, and each is questioned regarding the crime. One makes three truthful statements; one makes no truthful statements; how one suspect responds is unknown. From the following statements made by the three suspects, determine which one is guilty.

A: 1. I did not do it.
    2. I always speak truthfully.
    3. I do not believe it is natural to travel in space.
B: 1. I did not do it.
    2. My statements are all false.
    3. I do not believe it is natural to travel in space.
C: 1. I did not do it.
    2. Only one of my statements is false.
    3. I would like to go with the space travellers when they leave.

(Hints on page 77)
(Solution on page 101)

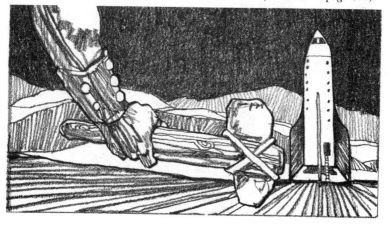

P2–10   Saddle Theft**

On several occasions recently, huffalon saddles have been discovered missing from the Village Saddle and Cart Company and there is sufficient evidence to conclude that a thief has been at work.

The list of suspected thieves has been narrowed to four employees. All four were on duty during the times that the thefts occurred.

The four suspects make the following statements, several of which are false. In fact, no two of the four make the same number of true statements.

A: 1. B is the guilty one.
   2. I was on a fishing trip during the last theft.
   3. No one thinks I am guilty.
B: 1. A is lying; I am not the guilty one.
   2. C has been on duty during every theft.
   3. D is guilty.
C: 1. B's first statement is true.
   2. I agree with A's first statement.
   3. I am not guilty.
D: 1. A's alibi is false.
   2. All of C's statements are false.
   3. I would not think of committing the crime.

Which of the four suspects is guilty?

(Hints on page 77)
(Solution on pages 101–102)

—3—
The Mixed-Up Mathematician

The Mixed-Up Mathematician sees nothing wrong with the eight mathematical problems he has prepared in this section. However, he has a linguistic quirk that is a form of transmogrification: He replaces digits with letters.

Your task is to fix the Mixed-Up Mathematician's problems by identifying the correct digits for each one.

P3-1 Subtraction, Five Digits*

Each digit in this problem has been replaced by a letter. Each letter represents the same digit wherever it occurs. There are no odd digits.

```
  A  S  S  S
- E  A  C  E
  E  A  S  Y
```

Determine the digit represented by each letter.

(Hints on page 77)
(Solution on page 102)

P3-2 Multiplication, Five Digits*

The multiplication problem below contains letters that have been substituted for digits. Each letter represents the same digit wherever it occurs. The digits are all odd.

```
  E  A  C  A  D
           ×  D
  ────────────
  A  E  E  A  D  B
```

Identify the digit represented by each letter.

(Hints on page 78)
(Solution on pages 102–103)

P3–3   Addition, Six Digits*

Each digit in this addition problem has been replaced by a letter. There are six digits: 0, 1, 2, 3, 4 and 5, and each letter represents the same digit wherever it occurs.

```
    F  F  C
    D  F  C
 +  D  D  B
 ─────────
 A  E  D  B
```

Determine the digit represented by each letter.

(Hints on page 78)
(Solution on page 103)

P3–4   Subtraction, Seven Digits**

The seven digits in this subtraction problem are 0, 1, 2, 3, 4, 5 and 6. Each letter represents the same digit wherever it occurs.

```
 D  A  D  C  B
 -  E  B  E  G
 ────────────
    B  F  E  G
```

What digit is represented by each letter?

(Hints on page 78)
(Solution on page 104)

P3–5   Multiplication, Nine Digits**

This multiplication problem contains letters representing digits. Each letter represents the same digit whenever it occurs. One of the ten digits, from 0 to 9, is missing.

```
      G  A  C  K  H
              ×  G  H
      B  J  G  D  H
   G  A  C  K  H
   K  C  J  F  G  H
```

Determine the digits represented by the nine letters.

(Hints on page 78)
(Solution on pages 104–105)

P3–6   Subtraction, Ten Digits**

This is a subtraction problem in which the digits are represented by letters. Each letter stands for the same digit whenever it occurs.

```
   G  J  A  B  F  E  F  H
 − H  G  D  K  J  F  D
   C  G  D  D  D  F  D
```

Solve this problem by identifying the digit representing each letter.

(Hints on page 78)
(Solution on pages 105–106)

P3-7   Multiplication, Ten Digits**

Each letter in the problem below has been substituted for one of the ten digits and represents the same digit wherever it occurs.

What number is represented by each letter?

```
        G H F
      × J E F
      ───────
        A J F
      J D E
    F B D
    ─────────
    F C A K F
```

(Hints on page 78)
(Solution on pages 106–107)

P3–8   Addition, Ten Digits***

This addition problem contains letters representing digits 0 to 9. Wherever a letter occurs, it represents the same digit. There are two possible solutions to this problem. Can you determine both answers?

```
      J  E  H  J
      C  A  E  H  F
   +  J  E  E  B  K
   ─────────────────
   J  D  K  D  B  G
```

(Hints on page 78)
(Solution on pages 108–109)

—4—
The Land of Hyperborea

Hyperborea existed long ago, at a time when there were monsters, when it was believed that the world was flat and when the sun rose out of the eastern ocean and set in the western sea. It was situated north of Mount Olympus, home of the gods.

The Hyperboreans were much favored by the gods, especially Apollo. A happy people, they lived blissfully in a land of sunshine, abundance and everlasting springtime.

What is little known about the Hyperboreans is their unusual standards of veracity, which provide for a delightful, although sometimes frustrating, type of puzzle, as you will see.

P4–1 Who Is Lying?*

Hyperborea is divided into three regions. Those who live in the southern region are known as Sororeans and always speak truthfully; those who live in the northern region are known as Nororeans and always speak falsely, and those who live in the middle region are known as Midroreans and make statements that are alternately true and false, but in which order is unknown.

Apollo decides to visit the Hyperboreans, his most favored people, in disguise. He approaches three inhabitants and asks which region each represents. The three respond, as follows:

A: I am a Sororean.
B: I am a Nororean.
C: 1. They are both lying.
    2. I am a Midrorean.

Assuming that each represents a different region, which is the Sororean, which is the Nororean and which is the Midrorean?

(Hints on page 79)
(Solution on page 109)

P4–2   One to Answer for Three*

In order to establish meaningful dialogue with the inhabitants, it would be helpful to know who is speaking truthfully and who is not. With this in mind, Apollo, perplexed after his meeting with three Hyperboreans, decides on a slightly different tack. He approaches three more inhabitants and directs his attention to one of them, hoping for a more lucid response this time.

The three are known to be a Sororean, who always speaks truthfully; a Nororean, who always speaks falsely; and a Midrorean, who makes statements that are alternately true and false, but in which order is not known.

Apollo, much to his consternation, receives this response:

A: 1. I am not the Sororean.
    2. B is not the Nororean.
    3. C is not the Midrorean.

Can you determine which of the three is the Sororean, which is the Nororean and which is the Midrorean?

(Hints on page 79)
(Solution on page 110)

P4–3 Three Fishermen*

Three Hyperborean fishermen are known to be a Sororean, who always speaks truthfully; a Nororean, who always speaks falsely; and a Midrorean, who makes statements that are alternately true and false, but in which order is unknown.

Upon returning from a day of fishing, the three fishermen are engaged in conversation with a visitor. Although one of the fishermen apparently does not feel like speaking, the other two speak, as follows:

A: 1. There were not many fish in our nets today.
    2. B's job is to throw and retrieve the nets.
B: 1. My job is to operate the boat.
    2. We brought in many fish with our nets today.
    3. If C felt like talking, he would truthfully say that he is the Sororean.

Who is the Sororean, who is the Nororean and who is the Midrorean?

(Hints on page 79)
(Solution on page 110)

P4–4   Abacus Abhorrence*

Progress is coming to Hyperborea in the form of the abacus. While this will mean improved ability to count and to calculate, there is considerable concern among the inhabitants, as it will mean changes for many people.

Three Hyperboreans are discussing the new technology. The three are known to be a Sororean, who always speaks truthfully; a Nororean, who always speaks falsely; and a Midrorean, who makes statements that are alternately true and false, but in which order is unknown.

A: 1. C still counts using his fingers and toes.
   2. B needs to have his own abacus.
   3. I am not the Nororean.

B: 1. I do not need to have my own abacus.
   2. I am the Midrorean.

C: 1. I disagree with A's first statement.
   2. I am the Sororean.

Who is the Sororean, who is the Nororean and who is the Midrorean?

(Hints on page 79)
(Solution on page 111)

P4–5 Who Won the Chariot Race?*

Chariot racing is a favorite sport among Hyperboreans, and is very competitive. In a highly contested race, little distance separated the first three finishers, and there was disagreement as to which one was the winner.

Hyperboreans are either Sororeans, who always speak truthfully; Nororeans, who always speak falsely; or Midroreans, who make statements that are alternately true and false, though not necessarily in that order. Regarding the three chariot racers, which group or groups they represent is uncertain.

Based on the following statements, who won the race and to what group or groups do A, B and C belong?

A: 1. I was the winner.
　　2. B was second.
　　3. C was third.
B: 1. I was the winner.
　　2. I was well out in front all the way.
　　3. C was behind A and me.
C: 1. I was the winner.
　　2. A was far behind when I crossed the finish line.
　　3. B finished before A.

(Hints on pages 79, 80)
(Solution on page 112)

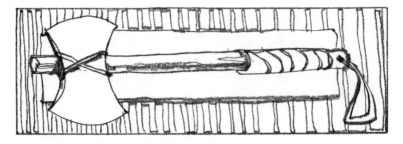

P4–6 Who Will Confront the Griffin?**

Even in a land as idyllic as Hyperborea, all is not always well. A griffin was in the land and was ravaging the flocks. Three shepherds were discussing which of them should confront the ferocious monster, which had the body of a lion and the head and wings of an eagle.

The three are known to be a Sororean, who always speaks truthfully; a Nororean, who always speak falsely; and a Midrorean, who makes statements that are alternately truthful and false, or false and truthful. The three shepherds make statements as follows:

A: 1. B does not even own a spear with which to confront the monster.
   2. C would faint if he had to confront the griffin.
   3. I am the only one who should challenge the ferocious monster.
B: 1. I do, too, own a spear.
   2. I am the Sororean.
   3. You cannot believe anything that C says.
   4. I will be the one to challenge the monster.
C: 1. I would not faint if I had to confront the griffin.
   2. I am the Midrorean.
   3. B is the Sororean.
   4. I agree with A's third statement.

Jupiter interposes to settle the problem and, with a wave of his hand, he makes the griffin smaller than a mouse. The three shepherds then chase it away.

Which shepherd is the Sororean, which is the Midrorean and which is the Nororean?

(Hints on pages 79, 80)
(Solution on page 112)

P4–7 Disagreeable D**

Four Hyperboreans are asked to which group or groups they belong. They respond below, although one of them is being disagreeable.

Inhabitants of Hyperborea belong to three groups: Sororeans, who always speak truthfully; Nororeans, who always speak falsely; and Midroreans, who make statements that are alternately true and false, but in which order is uncertain.

A: We each belong to a different group.
B: We are all in the same group.
C: 1. We are not all in the same group.
    2. I am in the same group as B.
D: 1. I disagree with A's statement.
    2. I disagree with B's statement.
    3. I disagree with C's first statement.

What group or groups are represented by the four Hyperboreans?

(Hints on pages 79, 80)
(Solution on page 113)

P4–8 Two Times Four Shepherds**

In every group of shepherds in Hyperborea, at least one is a Sororean, who always speaks truthfully, and at least one is a Nororean, who always speaks falsely. A visitor approached four shepherds on a hillside and asked each how many of the four were Sororeans. These answers were given:

—Three of us are Sororeans.

—One of us is.

—There are two of us.

—None of us are Sororeans.

The visitor approached four more shepherds on another hillside and asked how many were Nororeans. Their answers follow:

—We are all Nororeans.

—One of us is.

—Three of us are.

The fourth shepherd declined to speak.

How many of the shepherds on the two hillsides were Sororeans?

(Hints on pages 79, 80)
(Solution on pages 113–114)

P4–9 Mars Loses His Temper**

Four Hyperboreans were conversing with a visitor, who was actually Mars, god of war, in disguise. The visitor inquired as to their group or groups. Hyperboreans are: Sororeans, who always speak truthfully; Nororeans, who always speak falsely; and Midroreans, who make statements that are alternately true and false, although not necessarily in that order. At times the answers to questions put to Hyperboreans can be very frustrating. Mars, who had a short temper, turned all four into frogs.

Following are the responses that Mars received to his inquiry:

A: 1. I am either a Sororean or a Nororean.
   2. B is a Sororean.
B: 1. I am either a Sororean or a Midrorean.
   2. A is a Midrorean.
C: 1. I am neither a Nororean nor a Midrorean.
   2. B claims falsely to be either a Sororean or a Midrorean.
D: 1. I am a Sororean and A is a Nororean.
   2. I disagree with C's second statement.

To what group or groups do A, B, C and D belong?

(Hints on pages 79, 80)
(Solution on pages 114–115)

P4–10 Who Is to Be Transferred?**

Hyperborea is beginning trade with Ethiopia, which is located in the part of the known world that is south of Mount Olympus. It is rumored that, to establish a trade base, one or more Hyperboreans will be transferred to Ethiopia. Four Hyperboreans are discussing the subject. At least one is a Sororean, who always speaks truthfully; at least one is a Nororean, who always speaks falsely; at least one is a Midrorean, who makes statements that are alternately true and false, or false and truthful. Their statements follow:

A: 1. C said that D is going to be transferred.
   2. The food in Ethiopia is very good.
   3. I applied for the transfer, but I am badly needed here.
B: 1. The food in Ethiopia is not very good.
   2. C said that D is going to be transferred.
   3. A is a Sororean.
C: 1. I did not say that D would be transferred.
   2. D is a Nororean.
D: 1. A is going to be transferred.
   2. The food in Ethiopia is not very good.
   3. C said that I am going to be transferred.

Which employee is the Sororean, which is the Nororean, which is the Midrorean, and to which group does the fourth employee belong?

(Hints on pages 79, 80)
(Solution on page 115)

P4–11 An Outlier***

The land of Hyperborea has several well-established conventions to which all Hyperboreans should adhere. Certainly, their unusual standards of veracity are important to the land's traditions. There are the few odd inhabitants, though, who do not accept the value of conventions.

The following statements are made by four inhabitants, who are engaged in a discussion. One is a Sororean, who always speaks truthfully; one is a Nororean, who always speaks falsely; one is a Midrorean, who make statements that are alternately truthful and false, but in which order is uncertain. Some would say that one of the four is not a true Hyperborean. At any rate, this individual does not follow the customary rules of veracity and must be considered an Outlier.

Which one is the Sororean; which one is the Nororean; which one is the Midrorean; and which one is the Outlier?

A: 1. My statements are not all truthful.
   2. We are overworked.
   3. We are all lucky to be here.
   4. We Hyperboreans are favored by the gods.
B: 1. I agree with A's third statement.
   2. Every time I see a visitor, I think maybe it is one of the gods, in disguise.
   3. I am doing more than my share of the work.
   4. My statements are all truthful.
C: 1. My statements are all truthful.
   2. D's second statement is false.
   3. The gods do not visit us in disguise.
   4. We are all overworked.
D: 1. C's first statement is truthful.
   2. B's third statement is truthful.
   3. My statements are all truthful.
   4. The gods frequently visit us in disguise.

(Hints on pages 79, 80)
(Solution on page 116)

P4–12   Five Hyperborean Heroes***

Hyperboreans recognized heroes as those warriors who had single-handedly vanquished monsters. Each of five Hyperboreans, Actaeon, Ceyx, Minos, Nisus and Pyramus, had accomplished this feat. They defeated one sea serpent, two griffins (whose bodies were lions and heads and wings were eagles) and two chimaeras (whose foreparts were lions and hind parts were dragons).

All Hyperboreans are either Sororeans, who always speak truthfully; Nororeans, who always speak falsely; Midroreans, who make statements that are alternately truthful and false; or those few Outliers who do not abide by the land's traditions.

How truthful an Outlier's statements are is unknown, except that they are not the same as those who are Sororeans, Nororeans or Midroreans. As to the five heroes, little is known of their standards of veracity, except that one of them, and only one, is an Outlier.

Based on their statements below, can you determine the group of each hero, and what type of monster each defeated?

Actaeon: 1. Everything Minos states is false.
          2. I did not defeat a griffin.
          3. Ceyx defeated a griffin.
          4. I agree with Nisus' first statement.

Ceyx: 1. I defeated a sea serpent.
          2. Minos did not defeat a chimaera.
          3. Nisus defeated a chimaera.
          4. Actaeon defeated a griffin.

Minos: 1. I agree with Actaeon's first statement.
          2. Ceyx did not defeat a chimaera.
          3. Actaeon is not a Sororean.
          4. I defeated a sea serpent.

Nisus: 1. Minos' third statement is false.
          2. I defeated a chimaera.
          3. Actaeon did not defeat a griffin.
          4. Pyramus defeated a chimaera.

Pyramus: 1. Nisus defeated a sea serpent.
          2. Minos is a Midrorean.
          3. Actaeon is not a Nororean.
          4. Ceyx defeated a chimaera.

(Hints on pages 79, 80)
(Solution on pages 116–118)

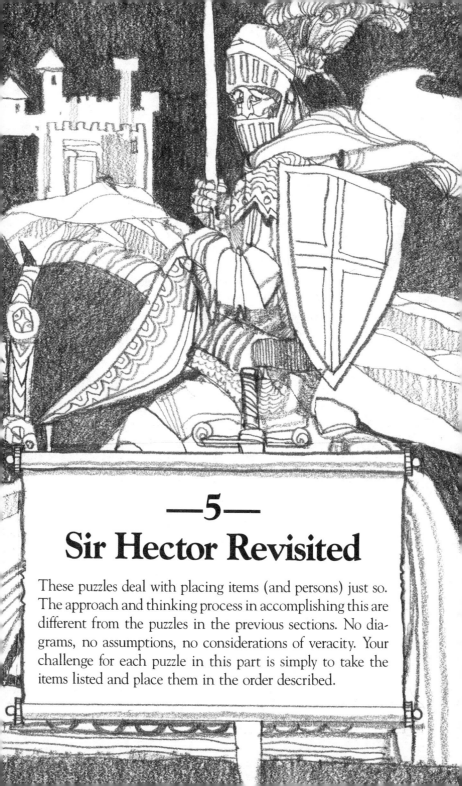

—5—
Sir Hector Revisited

These puzzles deal with placing items (and persons) just so. The approach and thinking process in accomplishing this are different from the puzzles in the previous sections. No diagrams, no assumptions, no considerations of veracity. Your challenge for each puzzle in this part is simply to take the items listed and place them in the order described.

P5–1   Sir Hector's Piscatorial Prowess*

In Sir Hector's time, part of the training of young men for knighthood involved instruction in recreational activities such as hunting, falconry, fishing, dancing and playing the harp. Sir Hector particularly enjoyed fishing during his spare time, and was proud of his skill at this sport. During one fishing season he caught at least one each of eight varieties of fish in five fishing excursions. Given the following information, what was the order in which he caught the eight varieties of fish?

The catfish was caught before the northern pike, but after the walleyed pike, which was caught before the muskellunge. The rainbow trout preceded the perch. The largemouth bass came after the muskellunge and the walleyed pike, which was caught during the second fishing excursion.

The perch and the northern pike were caught after the muskellunge, which was caught before the smallmouth bass, which was caught before the perch and the catfish, but after the rainbow trout, which followed the largemouth bass.

No fish were caught during the first fishing excursion of the season, and a total of only two fish were caught during the first three excursions. Fishing was especially good during the fourth excursion, in which the perch, the largemouth bass and the rainbow trout were among the fish caught. Two varieties of fish were not caught until the final excursion.

(Hints on page 80)
(Solution on page 118)

P5–2 The First Tournament*

A tournament was scheduled in the local province and seven knights, including Sir Hector, registered for the competition. It was agreed that every participant would joust with each of the others. Every knight's number of wins would be totalled to determine the winner and the rankings of the other six knights.

What was the order in which the players finished in the tournament, and how many jousts did each win?

—Sir Intrepid finished ahead of Sir Gallant and behind Sir Victor.
—Sir Able's ranking was an odd number, as was Sir Victor's.
—Sir Bold and Sir Able finished behind Sir Intrepid.
—Sir Staunch won four jousts.
—Sir Hector finished two places behind Sir Bold.
—Sir Gallant finished two places ahead of Sir Able.

(Hints on page 80)
(Solution on page 118)

P5–3 The Second Tournament*

Tournaments were a regular part of the activities of Sir Hector and his fellow knights. In one tournament, seven knights participated. Every knight jousted with each of the others and each joust counted one point for the winner. In one joust, the two knights fought to a standoff, so each was awarded one-half point.

From the statements below, determine the ranking of the combatants in the tournament (there were no ties) and the number of points each earned.

1. The one who finished in first place fought to a standoff with one of the others.
2. Sir Bold did not finish behind Sir Gallant.
3. Sir Gallant finished one point ahead of Sir Able, who finished two places in ranking ahead of Sir Staunch.
4. Sir Victor would have moved ahead of both Sir Hector and Sir Staunch if he had won his joust with Sir Hector.
5. Sir Intrepid finished behind Sir Staunch in number of points earned.

(Hints on page 80)
(Solution on page 119)

P5–4   The Third Tournament**

Knightly jousts and tilts have become quite popular in the province, and sixteen combatants participated in the most recent tournament.

Tournament rules provided that each knight would joust with one other participant. The winners would advance to the second round and each would joust with one of the other seven remaining knights. The third round would consist of the four undefeated knights, each jousting with one of the others. The tournament winner would be decided between the two combatants reaching the fourth round.

Based on the information below, list the participants who jousted in the second round, the third round and the fourth round, and identify the tournament winner.

Sir Resourceful won his joust with Sir Virtue, but lost to Sir Steadfast. Sir Gallant won his joust with Sir Victor, but lost his joust with Sir Resolute, who won against Sir Bold. Sir Hector won against Sir Staunch, but lost his joust with Sir Valorous, who won against Sir True. Sir Intrepid lost his joust with Sir Resolute, as did Sir Valorous.

Sir Able won against Sir Admirable, but lost to Sir Bold, who won his jousts with Sir Loyal and Sir Steadfast, who won his joust with Sir Faithful.

(Hints on page 80)
(Solution on page 120)

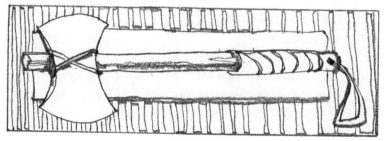

P5–5 Sir Hector's Knightly Accouterments**

As a youth, Hector was quite poor, and when knighthood was conferred upon him he could ill afford the weapons and armor of a knight. Therefore, he arranged to assist and perform routine services for the armorer until the value of the needed paraphernalia was earned. In this way, Sir Hector acquired his knightly accouterments, piecemeal.

Can you list the order in which he acquired his equipment, based on the information below?

The mail gauntlets were acquired before the battle ax, the sword and the lance, but after the boots and the dagger. The padded doublet, the shield and the breastplate were acquired before the visor, the mail hose and the shin guards, but after the sword sheath, which was acquired before the sword and the mail hood. The mail body armor was acquired before the dagger, the mail hose, the mail gauntlets and the battle ax, which was acquired before the sword sheath and the headpiece, which was acquired after the lance.

The sword was acquired before the mail hose, the breastplate and the visor, but after the padded doublet, the boots and the dagger. The padded doublet was acquired after the battle ax and the mail body armor, but before the shield, which was acquired after the breastplate. The mail hood was acquired before the lance and the shin guards, which were acquired before the lance.

The boots were acquired before the sword sheath and the mail gauntlets, but after the dagger. The mail hose was acquired after the shield and the sword sheath, but before the visor, which was acquired before the headpiece and the mail hood.

(Hints on page 80)
(Solution on page 120)

P5-6   Seasonings**

In Sir Hector's time, effective ways to preserve food were not available. There was considerable reliance on seasonings to enhance flavor and prolong freshness.

A travelling spice trader was set upon by thieves, who scattered his display of seasonings. Sir Hector happened on the scene and quickly routed the thieves. He offered to assist the trader in repositioning the seasonings on his display rack. The trader gladly accepted, and explained the order in which the seasonings should be placed in three rows on the rack.

Can you help by listing the 21 seasonings in their correct arrangement in the three rows? ("To the right or left of" means in the same row. "Above" or "below" means in the same column.)

The mace should be below the oregano and to the left of the cardamom, which should be above the thyme, which should be to the left of the basil and the rosemary. The cloves should be above the dillweed, to the right of the paprika, the oregano and the nutmeg, and to the left of the cinnamon, which should be above the rosemary. The tarragon should be below the cayenne and to the left of the thyme, the fennel and the garlic, which should be below the mace.

The cumin should be above the cayenne, to the right of the paprika and to the left of the oregano and the cinnamon. The rosemary should be to the right of the thyme and the fennel, which should be below the dillweed, which should be to the right of the mace, the poppy seed and the saffron.

The ginger should be above the cardamom, to the right of the oregano and the paprika, which should be above the saffron. The curry should be below the cinnamon, and to the right of the cardamom and the dillweed. The poppy seed should be above the basil, which should be to the right of the thyme, the garlic and the chili powder, which should be below the saffron.

(Hints on page 80)
(Solution on page 120)

—6—
Knowhey Land

This is a land of the future. The Knowheyan civilization is an advanced one, and the inhabitants are observed to be of great height and intelligence. A peculiarity of Knowheyans, however, is that they always speak in negative sentences, which, in itself, can be puzzling.

Because of the strange language spoken by the Knowheyans, an interpreter is provided to serve as guide in this section and to respond to questions that might be asked.

P6–1 Multiple Level Living*

The land of Knowhey is small and has a large population. Because of limited space Knowheyans live in multiple level residential buildings. Six inhabitants each occupy a different level in a six level building.

The interpreter explains, in typical Knowheyan fashion, which inhabitant lives on which level, as follows:

1. A does not live above the third level.
2. Neither C nor E lives above either D or F.
3. F does not live below A or B, and does not live above D.
4. E does not live below B or above A.

Which inhabitant lives on which level?

(Hints on page 81)
(Solution on page 121)

P6–2   Knowheyan Jobs*

Five Knowheyans, A, B, C, D and E, work in a metropolis as
Airfoil Technician, Communications Consultant, Space Plan-
ner, Lunar Energy Engineer and Synthetic Food Nutritionist.
No two of them are the same age.

The Knowheyan interpreter explains about the jobs and ages
of these five inhabitants, as follows:

1. The Communications Consultant is not younger than any
   of the other four.
2. D is not as old as A and not as young as B, who is not as old
   as the Lunar Energy Engineer, but not as young as C.
3. The Airfoil Technician is not younger than the Space
   Planner, who is not younger than the Synthetic Food
   Nutritionist.
4. C is not the youngest of the five.

What is the job of each of the five Knowheyans?

(Hints on page 81)
(Solution on pages 121–122)

P6–3   Knowheyan Art Fair**

Knowheyans are not negative by nature; it is just that their way of expressing themselves, using negative sentences, makes it appear that way.

Several fortunate visitors have an opportunity to attend the Midseason Art Fair, in which they are able to observe a variety of Knowheyan art forms. An artists' competition was held as a part of the fair and awards were given for the top four entries, which were collage painting, holography, laser etchings and reconstituted materials sculpture. The interpreter is explaining the results of the competition to the visitors:

1. A, who was not the first place winner, did not enter a holograph.
2. The fourth place winner did not enter a sculpture or a holograph.
3. The one who entered the collage painting, who was neither A nor C, did not win first or second place.

4. Neither B, nor the one who entered the laser etching, was the fourth place winner.
5. The third place winner was neither B nor C.
6. The one who entered the laser etching, who was not A, was not the second place winner.

What was the art entry of each of the four and in what order did they finish?

(Hints on pages 81–82)
(Solution on pages 122–123)

P6–4 Strange-Sounding Names**

The names of the inhabitants of Knowhey sound strange to the visitors, and they are difficult to pronounce due to their length and the few vowel sounds they contain. The Knowheyan guide is discussing the names of four inhabitants, whom we will refer to as A, B, C and D. Their names each contain up to eight syllables, although none of the four names contain the same number. Two of the names contain no vowel sounds; one contains one vowel sound; and one contains two vowel sounds.

From the guide's statements below, determine the number of syllables and vowel sounds in each of the four Knowheyan names.

1. The one whose name contains two vowel sounds is not A.
2. C's name does not contain more than one vowel sound or fewer than seven syllables.
3. The name with seven syllables does not contain exactly one vowel sound.
4. B and C do not have names with the same number of vowel sounds.
5. Neither the name with five syllables nor the name with seven syllables contains more than one vowel sound.
6. Neither the name with six syllables, nor B's name, contains two vowel sounds.

(Hints on page 82)
(Solution on pages 123–124)

P6–5 Transportation in Knowhey Land**

There are three principal means of transportation in the land of Knowhey: by foot, by private autojet and by public airfoil transit. Four Knowheyans commute regularly to the metropolitan center to work, and to attend cultural and sporting events. As is traditional on the planet, the four dress in bright, solid colors.

The Knowheyan interpreter is explaining to the visitors the method each uses to travel to the metropolitan center and the color in which each is attired. From the statements below, determine the method of transportation and dress color of each of the four Knowheyans.

1. Of the four, no two travel by foot or by private autojet.
2. Neither A nor B, who do not travel by private autojet, wears red.
3. The one who wears red does not travel by foot.
4. Neither the one who wears blue nor the one who wears green travels by private autojet.
5. Neither C, who does not travel by public airfoil transit, nor D wears orange.
6. D, who does not wear red, does not travel by foot.
7. The one who wears green, who is not B, does not travel by public airfoil transit.

(Hints on page 82)
(Solution on pages 124–125)

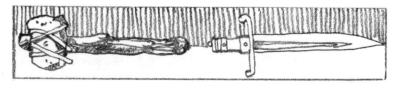

P6–6 The Game of Gulf***

Gulf is a popular game on Knowhey. It is played by hitting a small ball over long distances. The objective is to put the ball into a small hole with a minimum number of hits. The name of the game is derived from the land's terrain, which includes many extended inlets, or gulfs, over which balls must travel.

In an attempt to explain the game, the Knowheyan interpreter is describing, in negative Knowheyan fashion, the results of a game played by four inhabitants, A, B, C, and D. Each lost a different number of balls, and no player lost less than one or more than four.

1. The player with the highest score did not lose the fewest or the most balls.

2. The one with the second-lowest score, who was not D, did not lose more than three balls.
3. The player with the lowest score did not lose four balls.
4. The one with the highest score lost more than two balls.
5. B did not lose more than three balls or fewer than two balls.
6. The player who lost only one ball was not the one with the lowest score.
7. Neither D, who was not the one with the highest score, nor A, lost more than three balls.

What was the scoring order of the four players and how many balls did each lose?

(Hints on page 83)
(Solution on pages 125–126)

P6-7   Leisure Time***

The advanced technology in the land of Knowhey affords the inhabitants considerable leisure time. Four Knowheyans, A, B, C and D, each enjoy one of four leisure time activities: boating, music, reading and gulf (a game that involves hitting a small ball long distances, frequently over inlets, or gulfs, that extend far inland). The time from dawn to dusk is referred to as SP (Solar Period) and is measured in hundredths of SP. No two of the four spend the same amount of time in their leisure interests.

In response to a question regarding the four Knowheyans' leisure time and interests, the interpreter makes the following statements:

1. Neither A nor C plays gulf or is the one who spends .75 SP in leisure time interests.
2. The one who spends .6 SP in leisure time does not like boating.
3. The one who spends .9 SP in leisure time interests does not enjoy boating or music.
4. D does not play gulf, nor does A enjoy reading.
5. The one who enjoys boating is not the one who spends .5 SP in leisure time interests.
6. B does not spend .9 SP in leisure time interests.
7. The gulfer does not spend .5 SP in leisure time interests.

Can you determine which Knowheyan enjoys which leisure-time interest and the amount of time each devotes to the activity?

(Hints on page 83)
(Solution on pages 126–127)

Hints

H1   CHRONICLES OF SIR HECTOR

Puzzles in this section involve hypotheses. Your task is to review the statements in the puzzle and decide which ones to discard. For example:

1. If swimming is Jeff's favorite sport, then tennis is Henry's favorite sport.
2. If tennis is Henry's favorite sport, then basketball is Jeff's favorite sport.

From these two statements, there is one conclusion we can draw: The assumption in the first statement, that swimming is Jeff's favorite sport, is invalid when viewed in the light of the second statement. (This does not necessarily mean that the second part of the first statement is also invalid.)

H1-1   Giants or Dragons?: Two of the statements are valid and two are not. Construct a diagram such as the following:

	Sir Able	Sir Bold	Sir Gallant	Sir Hector
Giants				
Dragons				

Look for statements that are not consistent with any of the other three. Mark a minus sign where you reveal inconsistent assumptions.

H1-2   Encounter with the Black Knight: List the three possible outcomes, as below:

	Black Knight defeated	fought to a draw	fell in river
Outcome			

Pay particular attention to statement 4. Mark a minus sign where you identify invalid assumptions.

H1-3 The Fable of Sir Hector and the Giant: List the four possible outcomes, as below:

turned into a bird	was Mordin in disguise	retired to the mountains	totally collapsed

Carefully review the statements considering both the outcomes and the times of day. Mark a minus sign where the assumptions are invalid.

H1-4 A Victorious Encounter with a Dragon: Each statement refers to two knights. In each case, what was the role of the third knight?

Set up a diagram, as follows:

	fought	assisted	observed
Sir Able			
Sir Bold			
Sir Hector			

Mark a plus or minus sign according to whether each assumption is valid or invalid.

H1-5 Sir Hector's Steed: Construct a diagram, such as below:

	bay	black	black & white	grey	palomino	white
Charger						
Endeavor						
Valiant						

Carefully review and compare statements with the same names and/or the same colors. For example: comparing statements 3, 2 and 1, could the name be Valiant?

H1-6 Knights' Shields: Since there are four knights indicated and four color combinations, no two knights' shields are of the same color combination. The following diagram will be helpful:

	black & silver	blue & white	green & gold	red & white
Sir Able				
Sir Bold				
Sir Gallant				
Sir Hector				

Consider statement 5. Could Sir Hector's shield be blue and white?

H1-7 The Jousting Competition: Construct a diagram, such as below:

	winner	third unhorsed	second unhorsed	first unhorsed
Sir Able				
Sir Bold				
Sir Gallant				
Sir Hector				

Each statement mentions two or three of the four knights. In each case, consider the possibilities for the unmentioned knight or knights.

H1-8 Who Was Whose Squire?: A diagram will be useful in solving the puzzle. Give particular attention to statement 1.

	Alf	Bo	Cal	Del
Sir Able				
Sir Bold				
Sir Gallant				
Sir Hector				

H1-9 Which Knights Were Honored?: The diagram on page 75 will be helpful in organizing your conclusions:

	winner	3rd rank	5th rank	unranked
Sir Able				
Sir Bold				
Sir Gallant				
Sir Hector				
Sir Resolute				
Sir Victor				

Three knights were ranked and three were unranked. Compare statements 2 and 5. What can you conclude? Next, review statement 3. What can you conclude?

H1–10 Confrontation with Mordin the Sorcerer: The diagram below will be useful in organizing your conclusions:

	Sir Able	Sir Bold	Sir Gallant	Sir Hector	Sir Victor	pigs	goats	half knight /half goat
Sir Able								
Sir Bold								
Sir Gallant								
Sir Hector								
Sir Victor								

Note the sequence in which the knights were turned into different forms. From statement 4, could Sir Able have been turned into a half knight/half goat?

H1–11 Final Encounter with the Black Knight: A composite diagram, such as below, will be helpful:

	forest	plain	village	lances	staves	swords
first						
second						
third						
lances						
staves						
swords						

In each statement, only two weapons, locations and/or sequence of confrontations are mentioned. In each case, consider the possibilities for the missing weapon, location or number in the sequence of confrontations.

H2   THE PLANET DRANAC

For the puzzles in Part 2, construct diagrams listing the suspects on one axis and the statement numbers on the other, such as below.

	1	2	3
A			
B			
C			

Indicate T or F as you form conclusions about each suspect's statements. Assume that each suspect, in turn, is guilty; test each assumption against the truthfulness of all statements.

H2–1   Duplgoose Eggs: Three statements are false and one is true. Test this against your assumption regarding each of the four suspects.

H2–2   Huffalon Thefts: The two guilty ones make false statements; the others make true statements. Consider the possibility of each suspect in turn being guilty.

H2–3   Theft in the Overseer's Home: Note which suspects make two false statements, which one makes one true statement, and which makes two true statements. Test this against the statements made by A, B, C and D.

H2–4   Purloined Prickly Plum Pie: We know that the guilty one makes one true statement. Consider this as you assume each suspect in turn to be guilty.

H2–5   Theft on the Farm: Each suspect makes one true and one false statement. Consider this as you assume each suspect in turn to be guilty.

H2–6   Who Stuffed the Ballot Box?: Consider that each suspect makes only one true statement. Review C's statements. Could B be the guilty one?

H2–7   Theft in the Village Marketplace: Consider that no suspect makes more than one true statement. Assume that B is guilty. Test this assumption against statements made by the other suspects.

H2–8   Theft of the Produce Cart: Consider that no one of the three suspects makes all true statements. Test this as you make assumptions as to the guilty one.

H2–9   Attempted Sabotage: We know that one suspect makes all true statements and one makes all false statements. Consider this as you make assumptions as to the guilty one.

H2–10   Saddle Theft: Since no two suspects make the same number of true statements, we can conclude that only one makes three true statements. The challenge is to determine which one's statements can be depended on to be true.

H3   THE MIXED-UP MATHEMATICIAN

List the letters and then match the digits as they become known. Look for apparent digits that reveal themselves, by careful attention to numerical facts.

H3–1   Subtraction, Five Digits: The digits are 0, 2, 4, 6 and 8. Since there are only even digits, there will be no carries. Each number in the first row is larger than the number subtracted from it, otherwise there would be an odd number in the answer to the subtraction problem.

H3–2 **Multiplication, Five Digits:** The numbers in this problem are 1, 3, 5, 7 and 9. A, second letter from the right in the multiplicand, times D equals D. Work out the possible digits for A.

H3–3 **Addition, Six Digits:** The digits are 0, 1, 2, 3, 4 and 5. Consider the possible digits for A in the answer to the problem. Since C plus C plus B equals B, what are the possibilities for B?

H3–4 **Subtraction, Seven Digits:** The seven digits are 0, 1, 2, 3, 4, 5 and 6. What is the only possible digit represented by D, column (5)? Work out the possibilities for A, column (4). Remember, the largest digit available in the problem is 6.

H3–5 **Multiplication, Nine Digits:** The multiplicand is repeated when multiplied by G. What digit is G?

H3–6 **Subtraction, Ten Digits:** G, left side of the first line, disappears in the answer. Therefore, what digit is represented by G? There are two possible digits represented by A; what are they?

H3–7 **Multiplication, Ten Digits:** F times F equals F. There are four possible digits that could be represented by F. What are they? Two of them can be quickly eliminated when the products of F times H and F times G are examined. What are the two remaining possibilities?

H3–8 **Addition, Ten Digits:** What digit is represented by J in the answer to the problem? How about D, fifth letter from the right in the answer?

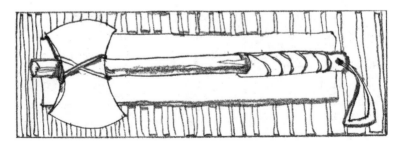

H4 THE LAND OF HYPERBOREA

The individuals in the puzzle section are true to their particular standards of veracity, without exception. For each puzzle, set up a diagram, such as the following:

	Sororean	Nororean	Midrorean
A			
B			
C			

Indicate plus or minus in the diagram as you confirm or rule out a particular standard of veracity for one of the statement makers. For example, if B states: "I am a Nororean" we know that B must be a Midrorean. We can draw this conclusion, since the statement would be truthful if made by a Nororean, and Nororeans always speak falsely. It would be false if it were made by a Sororean, and Sororeans always speak truthfully. Therefore, it must be a false statement by a Midrorean, since Midroreans make alternately truthful and false statements. Our diagram, at this point, would look like this:

	Sororean	Nororean	Midrorean
A			
B	−	−	+
C			

The process in solving the puzzles in this section is to test the possibility of each of the speakers being a Sororean, a Nororean or a Midrorean.

In puzzles **4–1**, **4–2**, **4–3**, **4–4** and **4–6**, one is a Sororean, one is a Nororean and one is a Midrorean; in puzzle **4–10**, a fourth speaker, of unknown veracity, is added.

In puzzles **4–11** and **4–12**, the additional complications of a fourth standard of veracity, that of an Outlier, has been added. An Outlier does not adhere to any of the three conventional Hyperborean standards. Therefore, an Outlier's statements must be, in some order, two truthful and one false, or two false and one truthful.

In puzzles **4–5**, **4–7**, **4–8**, **4–9** and **4–12** you are not told how many of each group are represented. The approach to solving them, however, is the same as when you know that one of each group is represented.

For puzzle **4–8, Two Times Four Shepherds**, the following diagram is suggested:

| | Group 1 | | Group 2 | |
	Sororean	Nororean	Sororean	Nororean
1				
2				
3				
4				

For puzzle **4–12, Five Hyperborean Heroes**, this diagram is suggested:

	Sororean	Nororean	Midrorean	Outlier	Monster
Actaeon					
Ceyx					
Minos					
Nisus					
Pyramus					

H5   SIR HECTOR REVISITED

These puzzles involve arranging things or persons in their correct order.

To solve these puzzles, list the items generally in the order described. Then carefully review the information given, and adjust the order of the items listed. Continue to readjust the order until it is completely consistent with the data provided in the problem. For most puzzles, this will require a number of realignments.

H6 KNOWHEY LAND

The statements in these puzzles are relevant, but each contains only bits of information. For each puzzle, a diagram will be helpful in organizing the pertinent data.

H6–1 Multiple Level Living: Prepare a diagram, such as below:

Level	
6	
5	
4	
3	
2	
1	

Indicate each inhabitant's level as you determine it.

H6–2 Knowheyan Jobs: The diagram below will be helpful:

	Airfoil Technician	Communications Consultant	Space Planner	Lunar Energy Engineer	Synthetic Food Nutritionist
A					
B					
C					
D					
E					

From statements 2 and 4, which one is the youngest?

H6–3 Knowheyan Art Fair: The following composite diagram will be helpful:

	Etching	Holography	Painting	Sculpture	1st	2nd	3rd	4th
A								
B								
C								
D								
1st								
2nd								
3rd								
4th								

From statements 2 and 4, which entry won the fourth place?

H6–4   Strange-Sounding Names: Construct the following diagram:

	Syllables				Vowel Sounds		
	5	6	7	8	0	1	2
A							
B							
C							
D							
0							
1							
2							

One of the inhabitants' names contains two vowel sounds. From statements 5 and 6, how many syllables are in that name?

H6–5   Transportation in Knowhey Land: Construct a diagram, as below:

	Foot	Public Airfoil	Private Autojet	Blue	Green	Orange	Red
A							
B							
C							
D							
Blue							
Green							
Orange							
Red							

From statements 2 and 6, which one wears red?

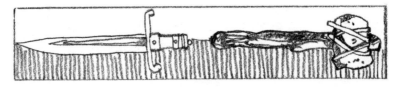

H6–6 The Game of Gulf: Prepare a diagram, such as below:

	Scoring Order				Balls Lost			
	Low	2nd Low	3rd Low	High	1	2	3	4
A								
B								
C								
D								
1								
2								
3								
4								

From statements 1 and 4, how many balls did the one with the highest score lose?

H6–7 Leisure Time: The following diagram will be helpful:

	Activity				Time			
	Music	Gulf	Reading	Boating	.5	.6	.75	.9
A								
B								
C								
D								
.5								
.6								
.75								
.9								

From statements 1 and 4, which one plays gulf?

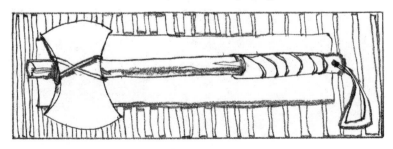

Solutions

S1–1   GIANTS OR DRAGONS?

CONSIDERATIONS:
Since two knights preferred giants and two preferred dragons, two of the hypotheses are valid and two are not.

Assume that the hypothesis in statement 1, that Sir Hector preferred giants, is valid. If so, then the conclusion that Sir Bold and Sir Gallant preferred dragons is true. However, if so, the hypothesis in statement 4, that Sir Able preferred giants, should lead to the same conclusion. It, however, concludes that Sir Hector and Sir Gallant preferred dragons.

Statements 2 and 4 are the only two containing hypotheses leading to the same conclusion. They are both valid.

	Sir Able	Sir Bold	Sir Gallant	Sir Hector
giants	+	+	−	−
dragons	−	−	+	+

SUMMARY SOLUTION:
Sir Able and Sir Bold preferred giants.
Sir Gallant and Sir Hector preferred dragons.

S1–2   ENCOUNTER WITH THE BLACK KNIGHT

CONSIDERATIONS:
From statement 4, the Black Knight vowed revenge, provided the two knights fought to a draw. Therefore, the assumption in statement 1, that the Black Knight was defeated by Sir Hector, is not valid.

From statement 2, the two knights fighting to a draw depends on an agreement that they would not fight again. Therefore, from statement 4, the two knights did not fight to a draw. The solution must be statement 3: Sir Hector fell in the river and managed to escape.

	Black Knight defeated	fought to a draw	fell in river
outcome	−	−	+

SUMMARY SOLUTION:
Sir Hector fell into the river and escaped.

S1–3 THE FABLE OF SIR HECTOR AND THE GIANT

CONSIDERATIONS:
From statement 3, if the giant turned into a bird, the battle took place at sundown. However, from statement 5, if the battle took place at sundown, the giant was Mordin the sorcerer in disguise. Therefore, the giant did not turn into a bird.

From statement 2, if the giant was Mordin, the sorcerer, the battle took place at sunup. However, from statement 6, if the battle took place at sunup, the giant turned into a bird. Therefore, the giant was not Mordin in disguise.

Also, from statement 5, since the giant was not Mordin in disguise, the battle did not last from daylight to dark. Therefore, from statement 1, the giant did not totally collapse and disappear.

Therefore, from statement 4, the remaining option, the giant retired to the mountains.

turned into a bird	was Mordin in disguise	retired to the mountains	totally collapsed
–	–	+	–

SUMMARY SOLUTION:
The giant left and retired to the mountains.

S1–4 A VICTORIOUS ENCOUNTER WITH A DRAGON

CONSIDERATIONS:
From statement 3, if Sir Hector fought the dragon, Sir Bold assisted. This would mean that the third knight, Sir Able, ob-

served. From statement 2, however, if Sir Able observed, Sir Bold fought the dragon. Therefore, Sir Hector did not fight the dragon.

From statement 4, if Sir Bold fought the dragon, Sir Able assisted. This would mean that Sir Hector observed. From statement 1, however, if Sir Hector observed, Sir Able fought the dragon. Therefore, Sir Able fought the dragon.

At this point our conclusions are:

	fought	assisted	observed
Sir Able	+	−	−
Sir Bold	−		
Sir Hector	−		

From statement 5, if Sir Hector assisted, Sir Able observed. Therefore, since Sir Able was the one who fought the dragon, Sir Hector did not assist. Therefore, Sir Bold assisted and Sir Hector observed.

SUMMARY SOLUTION: Sir Able fought the dragon.
                    Sir Bold assisted.
                    Sir Hector observed the battle.

S1–5 SIR HECTOR'S STEED

CONSIDERATIONS:
From statement 3, if the name was Valiant, the color was either black-and-white or black. However, from statement 2, if the color was black-and-white, the name was Endeavor. Therefore, if the name was Valiant, the color was black. From statement 1, if the color was black the name was Charger. Therefore, the name was not Valiant. From statement 6, since we know the name was not Valiant, the hypothesis is valid; the color was not white. Also, from statements 1 and 4, the color was not black.

From statement 2, if the color was black-and-white or palomino, the name was Endeavor. From statement 5, if the name was Endeavor, the color was bay or grey. Therefore, the color was not black-and-white or palomino.

Conclusions, so far, are:

	bay	black	black & white	grey	palomino	white
Charger		—	—		—	—
Endeavor		—	—		—	—
Valiant	—	—	—	—	—	—

From statement 7, if the color was bay or grey, the name was Charger. Therefore, since bay and grey are the two remaining colors, the assumption is valid; the name was not Endeavor. Therefore, the name was Charger. From statement 4, the color was grey, since we know it was not palomino.

SUMMARY SOLUTION:
The name was Charger; the color was grey.

S1–6 KNIGHTS' SHIELDS

CONSIDERATIONS:
From statement 5, if Sir Hector's shield was a color other than green and gold, Sir Able's shield was blue and white. Therefore, it is not possible for Sir Hector's shield to be blue and white, since those colors would belong to Sir Able's shield. It follows from statement 3 that Sir Bold's shield was not blue and white, since, if Sir Hector's shield was black and silver (or any colors other than green and gold), Sir Able's shield would be blue and white. From statement 6, since Sir Bold's shield was not blue and white, Sir Able's shield was not black and silver. Therefore, from statement 1, Sir Gallant's shield was not blue and white. Therefore, Sir Able's shield was blue and white.

From statement 2, if Sir Bold's shield was green and gold, Sir Hector's shield was blue and white. Therefore, Sir Bold's shield was not green and gold. It follows from statement 7 that, since Sir Bold's shield was not green and gold, Sir Gallant's shield was not black and silver.

Our conclusions so far are:

	black & silver	blue & white	green & gold	red & white
Sir Able	–	+	–	–
Sir Bold		–	–	
Sir Gallant	–	–		
Sir Hector		–		

At this point there are two choices for the colors of Sir Gallant's shield: green and gold, and red and white. From statement 4, if Sir Hector's shield was red and white, Sir Gallant's shield was not green and gold. Therefore, Sir Gallant's shield was red and white. Therefore, Sir Hector's shield was green and gold, and Sir Bold's shield was black and silver. (Note: Statement 5 indicates that if Sir Hector's shield was not green and gold, Sir Able's shield was blue and white. The assumption in this statement, that Sir Hector's shield was not green and gold, was found to be invalid. The conclusion that the assumption was invalid, however, does not preclude Sir Able's shield from being blue and white.)

SUMMARY SOLUTION:
Sir Able's shield: blue and white
Sir Bold's shield: black and silver
Sir Gallant's shield: red and white
Sir Hector's shield: green and gold

S1–7   THE JOUSTING COMPETITION

CONSIDERATIONS:
From statement 4, if Sir Able was the winner, Sir Hector was neither the second nor the first to be unhorsed. If this is the case, Sir Gallant was either the second or the first to be unhorsed. However, from statement 1, if Sir Gallant was either the second or the first to be unhorsed, Sir Able was the third to be unhorsed. Therefore, Sir Able was not the winner.

From statement 5, if Sir Able was the third to be unhorsed, Sir Bold was the winner or the second to be unhorsed. If so, either Sir Gallant or Sir Hector was the first to be unhorsed. However, from statement 2, if Sir Gallant or Sir Hector was the first to be unhorsed, Sir Bold was the third to be unhorsed. Therefore, Sir Able was not the third to be unhorsed.

From statement 6, if Sir Bold was either the winner or the third to be unhorsed, Sir Hector was the second to be unhorsed and Sir Gallant was the first to be unhorsed. However, since we know that Sir Able was neither the winner nor the third to be unhorsed, that knight must have been either the second or first to be unhorsed. Therefore, Sir Bold was neither the winner nor the third to be unhorsed.

Our conclusions, so far, are:

	Winner	third unhorsed	second unhorsed	first unhorsed
Sir Able	—	—		
Sir Bold	—	—		
Sir Gallant				
Sir Hector				

From statement 7, if Sir Able was the first unhorsed, Sir Gallant was neither the winner nor the third to be unhorsed. Since we know that Sir Able and Sir Bold were the first two knights to be unhorsed, Sir Gallant must have been either the winner or the third unhorsed. Therefore, Sir Able was not the first knight unhorsed; he must have been the second knight unhorsed, and Sir Bold was the first unhorsed.

From statement 3, if Sir Bold was the first to be unhorsed, Sir Hector was the third to be unhorsed. Since we know the assumption to be valid, Sir Hector was the third to be unhorsed and Sir Gallant was the winner.

SUMMARY SOLUTION: winner: Sir Gallant
third unhorsed: Sir Hector
second unhorsed: Sir Able
first unhorsed: Sir Bold

S1–8   WHO WAS WHOSE SQUIRE?

CONSIDERATIONS:
From statement 1, since either Alf or Del was Sir Hector's squire, neither Bo nor Cal was Sir Hector's squire. It follows from statements 4 and 6, that Del was neither Sir Able's nor Sir Bold's squire. From statement 5, Cal was not Sir Able's squire, and from statement 2, since either Del or Alf was Sir Hector's squire (statement 1), Alf was not Sir Able's squire. Therefore, Bo was Sir Able's squire.

Our conclusions at this point are:

	Alf	Bo	Cal	Del
Sir Able	−	+	−	−
Sir Bold		−		−
Sir Gallant		−		
Sir Hector		−	−	

From statement 3, since Del was not Sir Bold's squire, Cal must be Sir Gallant's squire. Therefore, Del was Sir Hector's squire and Alf was Sir Bold's squire.

SUMMARY SOLUTION: Sir Able's squire was Bo.
Sir Bold's squire was Alf.
Sir Gallant's squire was Cal.
Sir Hector's squire was Del.

S1–9   WHICH KNIGHTS WERE HONORED?

CONSIDERATIONS:
Statement 2 indicates that Sir Hector was the winner, unless Sir Able had to sit out a series of jousts. However, statement 5 indicates that Sir Able was the winner, unless Sir Hector had to remount his horse. Therefore, neither Sir Hector nor Sir Able was the winner. Further, since the five knights who were ranked entered every series of jousts and were not unhorsed at any time, neither Sir Hector nor Sir Able was among those who were ranked.

From statement 3, if Sir Victor was not ranked fifth, Sir Bold and Sir Gallant were not among the five knights who were ranked. However, we know that of the six identified knights, three were among those who were ranked. Also, we know that Sir Hector and Sir Able were unranked. Therefore, only one of the remaining four knights did not achieve a ranking. Therefore, Sir Victor was ranked fifth.

At this point our conclusions are:

	winner	3rd rank	5th rank	unranked
Sir Able	−	−	−	+
Sir Bold			−	
Sir Gallant			−	
Sir Hector	−	−	−	+
Sir Resolute			−	
Sir Victor	−	−	+	−

From statement 1, if Sir Gallant was the winner, Sir Bold was ranked third. If so, Sir Resolute must have been unranked. However, from statement 4, if Sir Resolute was not ranked, then Sir Bold was the winner. Therefore, Sir Gallant was not the winner.

From statement 7, if Sir Resolute was the winner, Sir Bold ranked fifth. However, since we know that Sir Victor was ranked fifth, Sir Resolute was not the winner. Therefore, Sir Bold was the winner.

From statement 6, if Sir Resolute was ranked third, Sir Victor was the winner. However, since we know that Sir Victor was ranked fifth, Sir Resolute was not ranked third. Therefore, Sir Resolute was unranked and Sir Gallant was ranked third.

SUMMARY SOLUTION: Sir Able   unranked
                     Sir Bold   winner
                     Sir Gallant   third in rank
                     Sir Hector   unranked
                     Sir Resolute   unranked
                     Sir Victor   fifth in rank

CONSIDERATIONS:

According to statement 4, Sir Hector was not overcome at the same time as Sir Able. Therefore, Sir Hector and Sir Able did not meet the same fate. Also from statement 4, Sir Able was not overcome at a later time than Sir Bold. Therefore, Sir Able was either turned into a pig or a goat.

According to statement 2, if Sir Victor was not turned into a goat, Sir Able was turned into a pig. From statement 1, Sir Gallant was not turned into a pig. The possibilities of knights who were turned into pigs are: Sir Able, Sir Hector (if Sir Able was turned into a goat), Sir Bold (if Sir Able was also turned into a pig) and Sir Victor (if Sir Able was also turned into a pig). Considering the alternatives, it is clear that Sir Able was turned into a pig. Therefore, Sir Able and Sir Gallant did not meet the same fate. Also, it follows that Sir Hector was not turned into a pig.

According to statement 1, if Sir Hector and Sir Bold met the same fate, Sir Able and Sir Gallant met the same fate. However, since we know that Sir Able and Sir Gallant did not meet the same fate, neither did Sir Hector and Sir Bold.

Our conclusions at this point are:

	Sir Able	Sir Bold	Sir Gallant	Sir Hector	Sir Victor	pigs	goats	half knight /half goat
Sir Able	−		−	−		+	−	−
Sir Bold		−		−				
Sir Gallant	−		−		−			
Sir Hector	−	−		−	−			
Sir Victor					−			

According to statement 5, if Sir Hector and Sir Victor met the same fate, so did Sir Gallant and Sir Bold. However, in this case, Sir Hector and Sir Victor would have been turned into pigs, and, since we know that Sir Able was turned into a pig, Sir Hector and Sir Victor did not meet the same fate.

According to statement 3, if Sir Hector and Sir Gallant met the same fate, Sir Victor was turned into a goat. However, in this case, all three knights would have been turned into goats. Therefore, Sir Hector and Sir Gallant did not meet the same fate. Therefore, Sir Hector was the knight who was turned into a half knight/half goat.

According to statement 6, if Sir Victor and Sir Gallant met the same fate, Sir Hector was turned into a pig. Therefore, since we know that Sir Hector was not turned into a pig, Sir Victor and Sir Gallant did not meet the same fate. Therefore, the two knights who were turned into pigs were Sir Able and Sir Victor, and the two knights who were turned into goats were Sir Gallant and Sir Bold.

SUMMARY SOLUTION: **Sir Able and Sir Victor: pigs**
                      Sir Bold and Sir Gallant: goats
                      Sir Hector: half knight
                      /half goat

S1–11   FINAL ENCOUNTER WITH THE BLACK KNIGHT

CONSIDERATIONS:
Assume that the first confrontation was not deep in the forest, as indicated by the hypothesis in statement 6. If this assumption is valid, the second confrontation was on the open plain (as indicated), the first confrontation must have been in the village of Farmwell, and the third confrontation was deep in the forest. However, from statement 1, for the second confrontation to be on the open plain, the third confrontation must be in the village of Farmwell, and it follows that the first confrontation must be deep in the forest. Therefore, we can conclude that the assumption in statement 6 is not correct; the first confrontation was deep in the forest.

Assume that staves were not used in the village, as indicated in statement 4. If not, staves must have been used on the open plain, since statement 4 indicates that swords would have been used in the forest. However, from statement 2, if swords were used in the forest, lances were not used in the village, and must have been used in the open plain. Therefore, staves must have been used in the village, and not in the first confrontation (which was in the forest).

Statement 3 indicates that if staves were not used in the first confrontation (which we know to be accurate), then lances were not used in the second confrontation. Therefore, lances were used in the first or third confrontation.

At this point, our conclusions are:

	forest	plain	village	lances	staves	swords
first	+	−	−		−	
second	−		−			
third	−					
lances			−			
staves	−	−	+			
swords			−			

From statement 5, since we know that lances were not used in the second confrontation, swords must have been used in the third confrontation. Therefore, lances were used in the first confrontation and staves were used in the second confrontation. Therefore, the village was the location of the second confrontation, and the open plain was the location of the third confrontation.

SUMMARY SOLUTION:

first confrontation:	deep in the forest	lances
second confrontation:	in the village of Farmwell	staves
third confrontation	on the open plain	swords

S2–1   DUPLGOOSE EGGS

CONSIDERATIONS:

Assume that D's statement is false. If so, neither A nor C is guilty. This means that either A's statement or that of B must be true. However, without additional information, we cannot determine the guilty one.

Therefore, since it was given that the guilty one can be deduced from the four statements, D's statement must be true. Therefore, the other three statements are false. C did not do it; the guilty one is A.

A	F
B	F
C	F
D	T

SUMMARY SOLUTION: A did it.

S2–2   HUFFALON THEFTS

CONSIDERATIONS:
Assume that A is one of the guilty ones and has made a false statement. If so, C is not guilty and has made a true statement. If so, D is not guilty and has made a true statement. If so, B is guilty and has made a false statement. If so, F is guilty and has made a false statement. If so, E is guilty and has made a false statement. Since there are only two guilty ones, and the assumption that A is guilty leads to four guilty ones, the assumption is incorrect.

Therefore, A's statement must be truthful. C is one of the two guilty ones and, since C's statement is false, the other culprit must be D.

A	T
B	T
C	F
D	F
E	T
F	T

SUMMARY SOLUTION: C and D are guilty.

S2–3   THEFT IN THE OVERSEER'S HOME

CONSIDERATIONS:
Since the housekeeper and the stable hand each make two false

statements, A must be the housekeeper and D must be the stable hand. Otherwise their first statements would be true.

C must be the huffalon groom, whose first statement is true and second statement is false.

B is the cook, who has made two true statements.

	I	2	job
A	F	F	housekeeper
B	T	T	cook
C	T	F	huffalon groom
D	F	F	stable hand

SUMMARY SOLUTION: A, the housekeeper, is guilty.

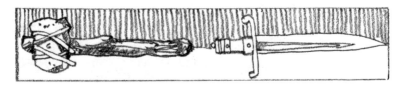

S2–4   PURLOINED PRICKLY PLUM PIE

CONSIDERATIONS:

Assume that A is guilty. If so, all three of his statements are false. Therefore, since the culprit makes one true statement, A must be innocent.

Assume that C is guilty. Since all three are known to be lovers of prickly plum pie, C's first statement must be false, as would be statements two and three. C is not guilty.

The guilty one is B. His second statement is true and statements one and three are false.

	I	2	3
A	F	F	F
B	F	T	F
C	F	T	T

SUMMARY SOLUTION: B stole the prickly plum pie.

S2–5   THEFT ON THE FARM

CONSIDERATIONS:

Assume that Farmhand No. 1 is guilty. If so, Farmhand No. 2's first statement is true and second statement is false. Farmhand No. 4 would also be guilty.

Since it was a given that there was one culprit, it is apparent that Farmhand No. 1 is not guilty. Therefore, Farmhand No. 2's second statement is true: Farmhand No. 4 did not do it. Farmhand No. 4's first statement is true and second statement is false. Farmhand No. 3 is guilty.

	1	2
No. 1	F	T
No. 2	F	T
No. 3	F	T
No. 4	T	F

SUMMARY SOLUTION: Farmhand No. 3 did it.

S2–6   WHO STUFFED THE BALLOT BOX?

CONSIDERATIONS:

B's first and third statements contradict each other. One is true and the other is false. Therefore, her second statement must be false. C did not do it.

C's second statement must be true. Therefore, his first and third statements are false. B did not do it. It follows that A is the guilty one by elimination. His second and third statements are false, and his first statement is true.

	1	2	3
A	T	F	F
B	F	F	T
C	F	T	F

SUMMARY SOLUTION: A is guilty.

S2–7 THEFT IN THE VILLAGE MARKETPLACE

CONSIDERATIONS:

Assume that B is guilty as indicated by B's second statement. If so, A's first statement is true. Either A's second or third statement, or both, are also true, or C's first and third statements must be true. Therefore, since at least two false statements are made by each suspect, B is not guilty.

Assume that A is guilty. If so, C's second statement is true. Either C's first or third statement, or both, are true, or A's second and third statements are true. Therefore, A is not guilty.

Therefore, C is guilty. A's first and third statements are false; B's first and second statements are false; C's first and second statements are false.

	1	2	3
A	F	T	F
B	F	F	T
C	F	F	T

SUMMARY SOLUTION: C is guilty.

S2–8 THEFT OF THE PRODUCE CART

CONSIDERATIONS:

Assume that A is guilty. If so, C's second statement must be his false statement. However, all of B's statements would be true. Therefore, since none of the suspects make all true statements, A did not do it.

Assume C is guilty. If so, all of A's statements would be true. Therefore, C is not guilty. Therefore, B is the guilty one.

	1	2	3
A	F	F	T
B	F	T	T
C	F	F	T

SUMMARY SOLUTION: B is guilty.

S2–9 ATTEMPTED SABOTAGE

CONSIDERATIONS:

B's second statement must be false. If true, it would be a contradiction. Therefore, B is not the suspect who makes all false statements. B must be the one whose standard of veracity is unknown.

C's second statement must be false. Therefore, C must be the suspect who always speaks falsely, and A must be the suspect who always speaks truthfully.

C's first statement is false. C did it.

	1	2	3
A	T	T	T
B	T	F	T
C	F	F	F

SUMMARY SOLUTION: C is guilty.

S2–10 SADDLE THEFT

CONSIDERATIONS:

Since no two suspects make the same number of true statements, we can conclude that only one makes three true statements.

All four were on duty during all of the thefts. Therefore, A's second statement is false.

C's first and second statements contradict each other; one is true and the other is false.

D's second statement is false, since at least one of C's statements is true.

B is the only one without a confirmed false statement. Therefore, all three of B's statements are true; two of C's statements are true; D's first statement is true; and none of A's statements are true.

	1	2	3
A	F	F	F
B	T	T	T
C	T	F	T
D	T	F	F

As indicated by B's third statement, D
is guilty.

S3–1   SUBTRACTION, FIVE DIGITS

CONSIDERATIONS:

(4)	(3)	(2)	(1)
A	S	S	S
− E	A	C	E
E	A	S	Y

For a puzzle of this type, list the five letters and match the digits
to them as they become known.

The five digits are 0, 2, 4, 6 and 8.

From column (4), since A minus E equals E, A must equal 4 or
8. From column (3), A must be 4 and S equals 8 (8 − 4 = 4).

Therefore, from column (4), E must equal 2 (4 − 2 = 2).

C, in column (2), equals 0 (8 − 0 = 8).

The remaining digit is 6; therefore Y equals 6.

SUMMARY SOLUTION:

$$\begin{array}{r} 4\ 8\ 8\ 8 \\ -\ 2\ 4\ 0\ 2 \\ \hline 2\ 4\ 8\ 6 \end{array}$$

A C E S Y
4 0 2 8 6

S3–2   MULTIPLICATION, FIVE DIGITS

CONSIDERATIONS:

	(5)	(4)	(3)	(2)	(1)
		E	A	C	A	D
					×	D
	A	E	E	A	D	B

The numbers are 1, 3, 5, 7 and 9.

A, column (2), times D equals D. Considering the alternatives,
A must equal 1 and, since there are no numbers to carry from
column (1), D must equal 3. Therefore, B equals 9.

Since the first digit in the answer to D times C is 1, C must equal
7 (i.e., 3 × 7 = 21).

A, column (4), times D equals 3 plus 2, which is carried from column (3). E equals 5.

SUMMARY SOLUTION:
$$
\begin{array}{r}
5\ 1\ 7\ 1\ 3 \\
\times\ 3 \\
\hline
1\ 5\ 5\ 1\ 3\ 9
\end{array}
$$

A B C D E
1 9 7 3 5

S3–3 ADDITION, SIX DIGITS

CONSIDERATIONS:

	(3)	(2)	(1)
	F	F	C
	D	F	C
+	D	D	B
	A	E	D	B

The letter A must be 1, as it represents a carry from column (3), which, even with a possible carry from column (2), must be less than 20.

C, column (1), could be 5 or 0, since the total of C plus C must be either 10 or 0 for the B in the third row to be repeated in the answer. However, F in column (2) is 5, as the D in the third row is repeated in the answer, indicating that there was no carry from column (1). Therefore, C is 0.

In column (3) we have the choice of 2, 3 or 4 being represented by D. If D equals 2, 5 plus 2 plus 2 plus a carry of 1 from column (2) would equal 10. However we know that 0 is already taken by C; E must be one of the remaining numbers. If D equals 4, 5 plus 4 plus 4 plus a carry of 1 from column (2) would equal 14. However, D and E cannot both be 4. Therefore, D must equal 3, and 5 plus 3 plus 3 plus a carry of 1 from column (2) equals 12. E, therefore, equals 2. The remaining digit is 4. Therefore, B equals 4.

SUMMARY SOLUTION:
$$
\begin{array}{r}
5\ 5\ 0 \\
3\ 5\ 0 \\
+\ 3\ 3\ 4 \\
\hline
1\ 2\ 3\ 4
\end{array}
$$

A B C D E F
1 4 0 3 2 5

S3–4 SUBTRACTION, SEVEN DIGITS

CONSIDERATIONS:
```
          (5) (4) (3) (2) (1)
           D   A   D   C   B
        –      E   B   E   G
          ─────────────────────
               B   F   E   G
```

The seven digits are 0, 1, 2, 3, 4, 5 and 6.

D equals 1, as D, column (5), becomes a carry to column (4), leaving no number in the problem answer. Since we know that D is 1, we can anticipate that D, column (3), takes a carry from A, column (4). Also, A is smaller than E, since it takes a carry from column (5). Therefore, A must be 2, and E and B are 6 and 5, or 5 and 6. (No larger number will work for A, as the largest number available in the problem is 6, and A, with a carry less a carry to column (3), becomes 11.)

B minus G, column (3), equals G. Therefore, since we know that B is either 5 or 6, B equals 6, G equals 3 (6 − 3 = 3) and E equals 5.

From column (2), it is apparent that C equals 0 (0 − 5 = 5). The remaining digit, 4, is represented by F.

SUMMARY SOLUTION:
```
     1 2 1 0 6     A B C D E F G
   –   5 6 5 3     2 6 0 1 5 4 3
   ───────────
       6 4 5 3
```

S3–5 MULTIPLICATION, NINE DIGITS

CONSIDERATIONS:

```
        G   A   C   K   H   (1)
      ×             G   H   (2)
      ─────────────────────────
        B   J   G   D   H   (3)
    G   A   C   K   H       (4)
    ─────────────────────────
    K   C   J   F   G   H   (5)
```

G must be 1, since row (1) is repeated in row (4).

K must be 2, since it represents the total of 1 represented by the G on the left end of row (4) plus 1, which is a carry from the addition of A and B.

H equals either 5 or 6, since these are the only digits which multiplied by themselves will yield the same digit, other than 0 or 1. If H were 5, the product of 5 times 2 (K) plus 2 carried from the first letter would be 12 and the second letter from the right in row (3) would be K. H, therefore, must be 6. D must be 5 (6 × 2 + 3 carried from the product of 6 × 6).

C must equal 0, since the product of 6 times C plus 1 carried from the second column equals 1.

F, in row (5), must equal 4 (1 + 2 + 1 carried from the previous column).

B plus A equals 10. A is either 7 or 3. If 7, the J from row (3) would be 2, but K is 2. A equals 3, B equals 7 and J equals 8. The missing digit is 9.

SUMMARY SOLUTION:

```
    1 3 0 2 6
        × 1 6
    7 8 1 5 6
  1 3 0 2 6
  2 0 8 4 1 6
```

A	B	C	D	F	G	H	J	K
3	7	0	5	4	1	6	8	2

S3–6 SUBTRACTION, TEN DIGITS

CONSIDERATIONS:

(8)	(7)	(6)	(5)	(4)	(3)	(2)	(1)
G	J	A	B	F	E	F	H
−	H	G	D	K	J	F	D
C	G	D	D	D	F	D

105

G, from column (8), must be 1, since a carry to the adjacent column leaves no remaining amount in the answer.

From column (2), it is apparent that F equals 0, since 0 is the only number that subtracted from itself will repeat itself in the answer. There is no carry to column (1), since the only possibilities for this would be D equals 6, 7 or 8, and a careful review of the possibilities for D in columns (3), (4) and (5) precludes these digits.

Since from column (1), H minus D equals D, we can conclude that H is two times D. Therefore, H is 4, 6 or 8, and D is 2, 3 or 4. However, D cannot be 2, since A, column (6), would also be 2. D cannot be 3, since then B, column (5), would have to be 7 and K, column (4), would also have to be 7. Therefore, H is 8 and D is 4.

From column (5), B must be 9, since B less a carry of 1 to column (4) minus 4 is 4.

A, column (6), is 2, since A minus 1 equals 1.

From column (3), E minus J equals 4. The only possibility, considering the numbers already taken, is that E equals 7 and J equals 3.

K, column (4), subtracted from 10, including a carry from column (5), equals 4. Therefore, K is 6.

C, column (7), is 5, since this is the remaining digit. This is confirmed by 13 minus 8 equals C.

SUMMARY SOLUTION:

A	B	C	D	E	F	G	H	J	K		
2	9	5	4	7	0	1	8	3	6		

```
  1 3 2 9 0 7 0 8
- 8 1 4 6 3 0 4
  5 1 4 4 4 0 4
```

S3–7   MULTIPLICATION, TEN DIGITS

CONSIDERATIONS:

```
          G  H  F   (1)
       ×  J  E  F   (2)
          A  J  F   (3)
       J  D  E      (4)
    F  B  D          (5)
    F  C  A  K  F   (6)
```

F equals 5 or 6, since F times F equals F; the other two possibilities, 0 and 1, can be quickly eliminated by comparing the products of F times H and F times G in row (3). If F were 5, there would be only two possible numbers represented by E in row (4) and D in row (5): 0 and 5. Since F would be 5, and D and E can't both be 0, F must be 6.

D plus D in rows (4) and (5) add up to 0 or 8, depending on whether there is a carry of 2 from J plus E. Since J plus E cannot equal 20 or more, D must be 0.

Since there is no carry forward from the product of F in row (2) times G, G must equal 1.

J from row (2) times F from row (1) leaves the digit 0. J must equal 5.

J (5), row (2), times H, row (1), plus a carry forward of 3, must equal less than 20, since the product of J, row (2), times G, row (1), equals F, row (5), which we know to be 5 times 1 plus 1 to carry equals 6. Therefore, H must equal 2 or 3, but if 3, B in row (5) would be 8, and 8 plus 5 would require a carry forward to F, left end of row (5), changing the resulting digit in row (6). H must equal 2.

Since E, row (2), times F, row (1), equals E, row (4), E must be 4 or 8. However, if E were 8, E times G, row (1), plus a carry forward, would not equal 5 (J); E must equal 4.

J, row (4), plus B, row (5), must be less than 10. B must be 3 and C must be 8.

J, row (3), plus E, row (4), is 9; K is 9, and A is 7, the remaining digit.

SUMMARY SOLUTION:

A B C D E F G H J K
7 3 8 0 4 6 1 2 5 9

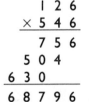

```
    1 2 6
  × 5 4 6
    7 5 6
  5 0 4
6 3 0
6 8 7 9 6
```

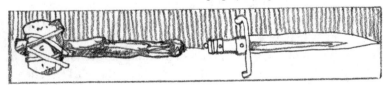

S3–8 ADDITION, TEN DIGITS

CONSIDERATIONS:

(5)	(4)	(3)	(2)	(1)
	J	E	H	J
C	A	E	H	F
+ J	E	E	B	K
J	D	K	D	B	G

J, left digit in the addition answer, is 1, since two digits, even with a carry from the adjacent column, will not equal 20 or more.

Since we have established that J is 1, a carry from column (4) to column (5) could not be more than 1. Therefore, D, column (5), which is the sum of C plus 1 plus a possible carry of 1, must be 0 or 1, considering that there is a carry of 1 from column (5). Therefore, D must be 0.

H, column (2), must be 5, since 5 is the only remaining number which, added to itself plus B, could equal B. Also, no number would work for H if there were a carry of 1 from column (1), and 1 plus F plus K could not equal 20 or more. Therefore, it is apparent that there is no carry from column (1).

E, column (3), is 3, as E plus E plus E plus 1 carried from column (2) equals 10.

From column (1), J (1) plus F plus K must equal less than 10, since we know there is no carry forward to column (2). Therefore, F plus K must equal 6 or 8. These are the only possibilities, since 0, 1 and 3 are taken. Therefore, K must equal 2, 4 or 6, and G must equal 7 or 9.

From column (4), J (1) plus a carry forward from column (3) plus A plus E (3) equals more then 10, since the smallest number available to A is 2 and the total would be greater than the largest number available to K: 6. Therefore, there is a carry forward to column (5) and C, column (5), must be 8, since C plus a carry plus J (1) equals D (0).

At this point there are two apparent numbers available to A: 7 and 9; no others will fit with the numbers available to K. Therefore, if A equals 7, K equals 2, G equals 9, F equals 6 and B equals 4. If A equals 9, K equals 4, G equals 7, F equals 2 and B equals 6.

SUMMARY SOLUTIONS: The two alternative solutions are:

```
  I 3 5 I              I 3 5 I
  8 7 3 5 6   or     8 9 3 5 2
+ I 3 3 4 2       + I 3 3 6 4
I 0 2 0 4 9       I 0 4 0 6 7
```

```
A B C D E F G H J K
7 4 8 0 3 6 9 5 I 2
or or       or or       or
9 6         2 7         4
```

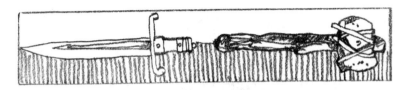

S4-1 WHO IS LYING?

CONSIDERATIONS:
B cannot be the Nororean as claimed, because that would be the truth, and a Nororean cannot speak truthfully. B cannot be the Sororean as the statement would be false, and a Sororean cannot speak falsely. Therefore, B is the Midrorean; A is the Sororean; and C, both of whose statements are false, is the Nororean.

The completed diagram is:

	Sororean	Nororean	Midrorean
A	+	−	−
B	−	−	+
C	−	+	−

SUMMARY SOLUTION: A: Sororean
                    B: Midrorean
                    C: Nororean

S4–2   ONE TO ANSWER FOR THREE

CONSIDERATIONS:

From statement 1, A must be the Midrorean. The statement would be false if made by the Sororean and true if made by the Nororean, neither of which would be possible.

Since statement 1 is truthful, and made by the Midrorean, statement 2 is false; B is the Nororean. Statement 3 is truthful and C must be the Sororean.

	Sororean	Nororean	Midrorean
A	−	−	+
B	−	+	−
C	+	−	−

SUMMARY SOLUTION: A: Midrorean
B: Nororean
C: Sororean

S4–3   THREE FISHERMEN

CONSIDERATIONS:

Assume that B's third statement is true. If so, then C is the Sororean, as indicated; B is the Midrorean; and A is the Nororean. B's second statement, however, would be false, making A's first statement true.

Therefore, B's third statement is false. C would not truthfully claim to be the Sororean. Therefore, A must be the Sororean; B is the Nororean, since his first and second statements are contradicted by A's statements; and C is the Midrorean.

	Sororean	Nororean	Midrorean
A	+	−	−
B	−	+	−
C	−	−	+

SUMMARY SOLUTION: A: Sororean
B: Nororean
C: Midrorean

S4–4 ABACUS ABHORRENCE

CONSIDERATIONS:

B's second statement is that he is the Midrorean. B is either the Midrorean or the Nororean, and, in either case, his first statement would have to be false.

A's second statement must be true, since it directly contradicts B's false first statement. Therefore, A's third statement, that he is not the Nororean, is true and A must be the Sororean.

Since A's first statement must be true, C's first statement must be false, since it directly contradicts A's statement. Therefore, C's second statement, that he is the Sororean, is false; C is the Nororean and B is the Midrorean.

	Sororean	Nororean	Midrorean
A	+	−	−
B	−	−	+
C	−	+	−

SUMMARY SOLUTION: A: Sororean
                                 B: Midrorean
                                 C: Nororean

S4–5 WHO WON THE CHARIOT RACE?

CONSIDERATIONS:

Assume that A was the winner. If so, A's first and third statements are true. However, A's third statement agrees with B's third statement, which means that B's first and third statements are true, as well, and B would also be the winner. Therefore, the winner must have been C, whose first and third statements are true.

C's third statement is consistent with A's second statement. Therefore, A is a Midrorean, whose first and third statements are false and second statement is true. B's second statement is inconsistent with our knowledge that the race was strongly contested, with the three finishing close together. Therefore, B, who has made three false statements, is a Nororean.

C's second statement, as with B's second statement, is false. Therefore C, whose first and third statements are true and second statement is false, is a Midrorean.

	Sororean	Nororean	Midrorean
A	−	−	+
B	−	+	−
C	−	−	+

SUMMARY SOLUTION: A: Midrorean
B: Nororean
C: The winner, Midrorean

S4–6   WHO WILL CONFRONT THE GRIFFIN?

CONSIDERATIONS:
Assume that B is the Sororean, as stated. If so, based on B's third statement C must be the Nororean. However, C's third statement indicates that B is the Sororean, which is inconsistent with B's third statement. Therefore, B's second statement must be false; B is not the Sororean.

Since C claims to be the Midrorean, C is not the Sororean; A must be the Sororean. Therefore, since C's fourth statement agrees with A's true third statement, C is the Midrorean, whose second and fourth statements are true, and first and third statements are false. Therefore, B is the Nororean, who has made all false statements.

	Sororean	Nororean	Midrorean
A	+	−	−
B	−	+	−
C	−	−	+

SUMMARY SOLUTION: A: Sororean
B: Nororean
C: Midrorean

S4-7 DISAGREEABLE D

CONSIDERATIONS:

A's statement, which implies the existence of four groups, is false, as we know there are three groups.

D's first statement is true, as it disputes A's false statement. Therefore, D is either a Sororean or a Midrorean and, in either case, D's third statement must be true.

Since D's third statement, which is true, disputes C's first statement, which disagrees with B's statement, we can conclude that B's statement is true. Therefore, all four Hyperboreans belong to the same group. Since C's first statement is false and second statement is true, and D's second statement is false, we can conclude that the four are Midroreans.

	Sororean	Nororean	Midrorean
A	−	−	+
B	−	−	+
C	−	−	+
D	−	−	+

S4-8 TWO TIMES FOUR SHEPHERDS

CONSIDERATIONS:

In the first group of shepherds, the statement "None of us are Sororeans" would have to be false. There was at least one Sororean in the group. Since there was only one statement indicating three Sororeans and one statement indicating two Sororeans, neither statement was truthful. There was one Sororean in the first group.

In the second group of shepherds, the statement "We are all Nororeans" would have to be false. There could be no more than three Nororeans. If the fourth shepherd had chosen to speak, he or she could not have given a truthful response: The statement "One of us is a Nororean" would suggest three Sororeans, but this would require a confirmation from two others. The statement "Three of us are Nororeans" could only be made truthfully by one shepherd (and it was). The statement "Two of us are Nororeans" would require the same statement by one of the other shepherds (it was not). Therefore, there were three Nororeans and one Sororean in the second group.

| | Group 1 | | Group 2 | |
	Sororean	Nororean	Sororean	Nororean
1	−	+	−	+
2	+	−	−	+
3	−	+	+	−
4	−	+	−	+

SUMMARY SOLUTION: There were two Sororeans in the two groups of shepherds.

S4–9 MARS LOSES HIS TEMPER

CONSIDERATIONS:

A's first statement contains two parts; if either is true, the statement is true. A is not a Nororean, as a Nororean cannot make a true statement. If the statement is true, A is a Sororean; if the statement is false, A is a Midrorean. In either case, A's second statement must be true: B is a Sororean.

B's second statement confirms that A is a Midrorean.

For C's first statement to be true, C would have to be a Sororean, but this is not possible because of C's second statement, which disputes B's first statement and is, therefore, false. Both of C's statements are false; C is a Nororean.

D's first statement is false, as A is not a Nororean. D's second statement, however, which disputes C's second statement, is true: D is a Midrorean.

	Sororean	Nororean	Midrorean
A	−	−	+
B	+	−	−
C	−	+	−
D	−	−	+

SUMMARY SOLUTION: A: Midrorean
                    B: Sororean
                    C: Nororean
                    D: Midrorean

S4–10   WHO IS TO BE TRANSFERRED?

CONSIDERATIONS:
Assume that B's first statement is truthful. If so, then B's third statement, that A is a Sororean, is also truthful. A's second statement, however, contradicts B's first statement.

Therefore, B's first statement must be false. This means that A's second statement is true, but, from B's third statement, which must be false, we know that A is not a Sororean. A's first and third statements must be false, and A is a Midrorean. Since B's second statement confirms A's first statement, which is false, B is a Nororean.

Since A's first statement is false, C's first statement is true.

D's third statement falsely confirms A's false first statement (as well as B's false second statement). D's second statement agrees with B's false first statement. Therefore, D is a Nororean. Therefore, C's second statement is true: C is a Sororean.

	Sororean	Nororean	Midrorean
A	−	−	+
B	−	+	−
C	+	−	−
D	−	+	−

SUMMARY SOLUTION: A: Midrorean
                      B: Nororean
                      C: Sororean
                      D: Nororean

S4–11 AN OUTLIER

CONSIDERATIONS:

A's first statement must be true. It would be false only for a Sororean. Therefore, A is neither a Sororean, since Sororeans always speak truthfully, nor a Nororean, since Nororeans always speak falsely. A could be a Midrorean, but, if so, the first and third statements would be true, and the second and fourth statements would be false. However, as is known to us, A's fourth statement is true. Therefore, A is not a Midrorean; A must be the Outlier.

Assume that D's third statement is truthful. If so, D is the Sororean. However, D's first statement agrees with C's first statement, which also claims all truthful statements. Therefore, since we know that there is only one Sororean, D's third statement is false, as is his first statement and, it follows, C's first statement as well. Therefore, neither D nor C is the Sororean. Therefore, B must be the Sororean.

D's second statement agrees with B's true third statement. Therefore, D is the Midrorean, whose second and fourth statements are true. C is the Nororean, who has made four false statements.

	Sororean	Nororean	Midrorean	Outlier
A	−	−	−	+
B	+	−	−	−
C	−	+	−	−
D	−	−	+	−

SUMMARY SOLUTION: A: Outlier
                    B: Sororean
                    C: Nororean
                    D: Midrorean

S4–12 FIVE HYPERBOREAN HEROES

CONSIDERATIONS:

Minos' first statement agrees with Actaeon's first statement, which

116

asserts that everything Minos says is false. If Actaeon's first statement was true, Minos could not agree with it. Therefore, it must be false, and, agreeing with it, Minos' first statement is also false. Therefore, neither Actaeon nor Minos is a Sororean. Also, since Actaeon's first statement is false, Minos is not a Nororean. He is either a Midrorean or the Outlier. If Minos is a Midrorean, his third statement would have to be false, but it is true: Actaeon is not a Sororean. Therefore, Minos, whose first statement is false and third statement is true, is the Outlier.

Nisus' first statement is false, since he disputes Minos' third statement, which we know to be true. Therefore, Nisus must be either a Nororean or a Midrorean; in either case, since his first statement is false, his third statement must also be false: Actaeon defeated a griffin. Since Actaeon's second statement denies this, Actaeon is a Nororean.

Pyramus' second and third statements are known to be false, and it follows that the first and fourth statements are also false. Pyramus is a Nororean. From Pyramus' first and fourth statements, which are false, we can determine that Nisus did not defeat the sea serpent and Ceyx did not defeat a chimaera.

Conclusions at this point:

	Sororean	Nororean	Midrorean	Outlier	Monster
Actaeon	−	+	−	−	griffin
Ceyx				−	not chimaera
Minos	−	−	−	+	
Nisus	−			−	not sea serpent
Pyramus	−	+	−	−	

From Actaeon's third statement, Ceyx did not defeat a griffin. Therefore, Ceyx must have defeated the sea serpent.

Ceyx's fourth statement, that Actaeon defeated a griffin, is consistent with Actaeon's second statement denying this, which we know to be false. Therefore, Ceyx's second statement is also truthful and Minos must have defeated the second griffin.

Nisus must have defeated a chimaera, and this is confirmed by his second statement. Therefore, Nisus' fourth statement, which asserts that Pyramus defeated the other chimaera, is also true. Nisus is a Midrorean.

Ceyx, who defeated the sea serpent, as claimed, is a Sororean.

SUMMARY SOLUTION:

Actaeon:	Nororean	griffin
Ceyx:	Sororean	sea serpent
Minos:	Outlier	griffin
Nisus:	Midrorean	chimaera
Pyramus:	Nororean	chimaera

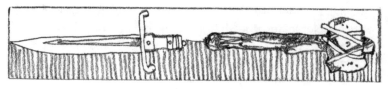

S5–1   SIR HECTOR'S PISCATORIAL PROWESS

SUMMARY SOLUTION:
1. Walleyed Pike
2. Muskellunge
3. Largemouth Bass
4. Rainbow Trout
5. Smallmouth Bass
6. Perch
7. Catfish
8. Northern Pike

S5–2   THE FIRST TOURNAMENT

SUMMARY SOLUTION:

Ranking	Knight	Jousts Won
1	Sir Victor	6
2	Sir Intrepid	5
3	Sir Staunch	4
4	Sir Bold	3
5	Sir Gallant	2
6	Sir Hector	1
7	Sir Able	0

S5-3 THE SECOND TOURNAMENT

CONSIDERATIONS:

Three conclusions can be drawn from statement 4:

1. Sir Victor must have finished one-half point behind Sir Staunch, since an additional win would have moved him ahead of Sir Staunch.

2. Sir Victor must have been the one who fought to a standoff with the first place finisher, as noted in statement 1, since a win over Sir Hector would have moved him past Sir Hector.

3. Since Sir Victor finished one-half point behind Sir Staunch, Sir Hector must have finished immediately ahead of Sir Staunch.

From statement 3, we know that Sir Gallant finished one place ahead of Sir Able, who must have finished immediately ahead of Sir Hector, since Sir Able was two places ahead of Sir Staunch. Also from statement 3, we can conclude that Sir Gallant was not the winner, since his rating placed him one point ahead of Sir Able, who could not have earned one-half point in any of his jousts.

Since Sir Intrepid finished behind Sir Staunch, he must have also placed behind Sir Victor, who was only one-half point behind Sir Staunch.

This leaves Sir Bold as the Winner. He tied in his joust with Sir Victor, who earned 1½ points in the tournament.

SUMMARY SOLUTION:

Place Finished	Knight	Number of Points Earned
1st	Sir Bold	5½
2nd	Sir Gallant	5
3rd	Sir Able	4
4th	Sir Hector	3
5th	Sir Staunch	2
6th	Sir Victor	1½
7th	Sir Intrepid	0

S5–4 THE THIRD TOURNAMENT

SUMMARY SOLUTION:

Round 2	Round 3	Round 4	Tournament Winner
Sir Able	Sir Bold	Sir Bold	Sir Resolute
Sir Bold	Sir Valorous	Sir Resolute	
Sir Valorous	Sir Resolute		
Sir Resolute	Sir Steadfast		
Sir Steadfast			
Sir Resourceful			
Sir Gallant			
Sir Hector			

S5–5 SIR HECTOR'S KNIGHTLY ACCOUTERMENTS

SUMMARY SOLUTION:

1. mail body armor
2. dagger
3. boots
4. mail gauntlets
5. battle ax
6. sword sheath
7. padded doublet
8. sword
9. breastplate
10. shield
11. mail hose
12. visor
13. mail hood
14. shin guards
15. lance
16. headpiece

S5–6 SEASONINGS

SOLUTION:

paprika	cumin	oregano	ginger	nutmeg	cloves	cinnamon
saffron	cayenne	mace	cardamon	poppy seed	dillweed	curry
chili powder	tarragon	garlic	thyme	basil	fennel	rosemary

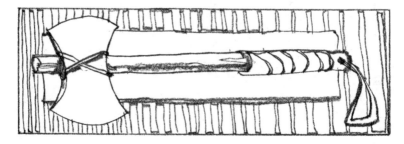

S6-1   MULTIPLE LEVEL LIVING

CONSIDERATIONS:
From statement 4, E lives above B and below A. From statement 1, A does not live above level 3. Therefore B, E and A occupy the first, second and third levels, respectively.

So far, we have:

Level	
6	
5	
4	
3	A
2	E
I	B

From statements 2 and 3, C occupies the fourth level, F occupies the fifth level and D occupies the sixth level.

SUMMARY SOLUTION:

	Level
A	3rd
B	Ist
C	4th
D	6th
E	2nd
F	5th

S6-2   KNOWHEYAN JOBS

CONSIDERATIONS:
From statement 2, A is the oldest among the four Knowheyans mentioned. Therefore, from statement 1, the Communications Consultant is either A or E, who is not mentioned in statement 2. From statement 4, C (who is the youngest among the four referred to in statement 2) is not the youngest of the five. Therefore, E must be the youngest. Therefore, A is the oldest, and the Communications Consultant.

Also from statement 2, it is apparent that D is the Lunar Energy Engineer.

Our conclusions so far are:

	Airfoil Technician	Communications Consultant	Space Planner	Lunar Energy Engineer	Synthetic Food Nutritionist
A	−	+	−	−	−
B		−		−	
C		−		−	
D	−	−	−	+	−
E		−		−	

Statement 3 indicates that of the remaining three, the Airfoil Technician is the oldest and the Synthetic Food Nutritionist is the youngest. Therefore, E is the Synthetic Food Nutritionist. B, who is older than C (from statement 2), is the Airfoil Technician, and C is the Space Planner.

SUMMARY SOLUTION:

A: Communications Consultant
B: Airfoil Technician
C: Space Planner
D: Lunar Energy Engineer
E: Synthetic Food Nutritionist

S6–3 KNOWHEYAN ART FAIR

CONSIDERATIONS:

From statements 2 and 4, the one who entered the painting was the 4th place winner. From statement 3, neither A nor C entered the painting, and from statement 4, B was not the 4th place winner. Therefore, D entered the painting and was the 4th place winner.

From statements 1 and 6, A did not enter either the holograph or the laser etching, so must have entered the sculpture. From statement 1, A was not the first place winner, and from statement 5, neither B nor C was the 3rd place winner. Therefore, A was the 3rd place winner:

At this point, our conclusions are:

	Etching	Holography	Painting	Sculpture	1st	2nd	3rd	4th
A	−	−	−	+	−	−	+	−
B			−	−			−	−
C			−	−			−	−
D	−	−	+	−	−	−	−	+
1st	−	−	−	−				
2nd			−	−				
3rd	−	−	−	+				
4th	−	−	+	−				

From statement 4, B did not enter the laser etching, and from statement 6, the one who entered the etching was not the 2nd place winner. Therefore, B entered the holograph and was the 2nd place winner. C entered the laser etching and was the first place winner.

SUMMARY SOLUTION:

	Entry	Finish Order
A:	sculpture	3rd place
B:	holography	2nd place
C:	etching	1st place
D:	painting	4th place

S6–4 STRANGE-SOUNDING NAMES

CONSIDERATIONS:
From statements 5 and 6, the name with eight syllables is the one with two vowel sounds. From statements 1, 2 and 6, D's name must be the one with eight syllables and two vowel sounds.

From statement 2, since C's name does not contain fewer than seven syllables and D's name contains eight syllables, C's name has seven syllables. From statement 3, C's name must contain no vowel sounds.

Conclusions so far:

	Syllables				Vowel Sounds		
	5	6	7	8	0	1	2
A			−	−			−
B			−	−			−
C	−	−	+	−	+	−	−
D	−	−	−	+	−	−	+
0				−			
1				−			
2				+			

From statement 4, since B and C do not have names with the same number of vowel sounds, B's name must contain one vowel sound, and, since we know that two of the four inhabitants' names contain no vowel sounds, A must be the other one with no vowel sounds.

From statement 6, since B's name does not contain six syllables, this number must belong to A's name, and B's name has five syllables.

SUMMARY SOLUTION:

	Syllables	Vowel Sounds
A	6	0
B	5	1
C	7	0
D	8	2

S6–5 TRANSPORTATION IN KNOWHEY LAND

CONSIDERATIONS:

From statements 2 and 6, C must be the one who wears red. Therefore, from statement 3, C does not travel by foot, nor does D, from statement 6. From statement 5, C does not travel by public airfoil transit. Therefore, C is the one who travels by private auto-jet.

Our conclusions, at this point, are:

	Foot	Public Airfoil	Private Autojet	Blue	Green	Orange	Red
A			−				−
B			−				−
C	−	−	+	−	−	−	+
D	−		−			−	−
Blue			−				
Green			−				
Orange			−				
Red	−	−	+				

From statement 7, A must be the one who travels by foot and wears green.

From statement 1, B and D must both travel by public airfoil transit. Since D does not wear orange, from statement 5, that color is worn by B, and the remaining color, blue, is worn by D.

SUMMARY SOLUTION:

	Method	Color
A:	foot	green
B:	public airfoil	orange
C:	private autojet	red
D:	public airfoil	blue

S6–6 THE GAME OF GULF

CONSIDERATIONS:
Statements 1 and 4 indicate that the one with the highest score did not lose one, four or two balls. Therefore, the one with the highest score lost three balls.

From statements 2 and 3, the one who lost four balls must have been the third lowest scorer.

From statements 2 and 7, since D was not the one with the second lowest score or the one with the highest score, and did not lose four balls, D must have been the player with the lowest score. From statement 6, D must have lost two balls. Therefore, from statement 5, B lost three balls and was the one with the highest score.

Conclusions, so far, are:

| | Scoring Order | | | | Balls Lost | | | |
	Low	2nd Low	3rd Low	High	1	2	3	4
A	−			−		−	−	
B	−	−	−	+	−	−	+	−
C	−			−		−	−	
D	+	−	−	−	−	+	−	−
1	−	+	−	−				
2	+	−	−	−				
3	−	−	−	+				
4	−	−	+	−				

From statement 7, A was not the one who lost four balls. Therefore, A lost one ball and was the one with the second-lowest score.

Therefore, C was the one with the third-lowest score and lost four balls.

SUMMARY SOLUTION:

	Scoring Order	Balls Lost
A:	2nd low score	1 ball lost
B:	high score	3 balls lost
C:	3rd low score	4 balls lost
D:	low score	2 balls lost

S6–7 LEISURE TIME

CONSIDERATIONS:
From statements 1 and 4, neither A, C nor D play gulf. Therefore, B is the one who plays gulf. From statements 6 and 7, B does not spend .9 SP or .5 SP in leisure-time activity. From statements 2, 3 and 5, the one who enjoys boating must spend .75 SP in leisure-time activity. Therefore, B spends .6 SP playing gulf.

Since B is the one who spends .6 SP in leisure-time activity and, from statement 1, neither A nor C spends .75 SP in leisure-time activity, D spends .75 SP time in leisure-time activity and is the one who enjoys boating.

At this point, our conclusions are:

	Music	Gulf	Reading	Boating	.5	.6	.75	.9
		Activity				Time		
A		−		−		−	−	
B	−	+	−	−	−	+	−	−
C		−		−		−	−	
D	−	−	−	+	−	−	+	−
.5		−		−				
.6	−	+	−	−				
.75	−	−	−	+				
.9		−		−				

Since, from statement 3, the one who spends .9 SP in leisure interests does not enjoy music, this amount of SP must apply to reading. From statement 4, A does not enjoy reading. Therefore, C is the one who enjoys reading and spends .9 SP in leisure-time interest.

Therefore, A enjoys music and spends .5 SP in leisure-time interest.

SUMMARY SOLUTION:

	Interest	Amount of Time
A:	music	.5 SP
B:	gulf	.6 SP
C:	reading	.9 SP
D:	boating	.75 SP

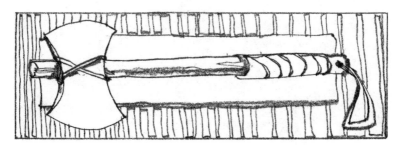

Index